Problem solving

JILL BENNETT and
ROGER SMITH

TEACHER TIMESAVERS

Published by Scholastic Publications Ltd,
Villiers House,
Clarendon Avenue,
Leamington Spa,
Warwickshire CV32 5PR

Author Jill Bennett and Roger Smith
Editor Margot O'Keeffe
Sub-editor Angela Dewsbury
Series designer Joy White
Designers Clare Brewer and Anna Oliwa
Illustrations Cathy Gilligan and The Drawing Room
Cover illustration Frances Lloyd
Cover photograph Martyn Chillmaid

Designed using Aldus Pagemaker
Processed by Pages Bureau, Leamington Spa
Artwork by David Harban Design, Warwick
Printed in Great Britain by Ebenezer Baylis & Son, Worcester

British Library Cataloguing-in-Publication Data
A catalogue record for this book is
available from the British Library.

ISBN 0-590-53010-0

Contents

ISBN, price and blurb. The children should include these features in their design.
Save Sam! Encourage the children to be as inventive as possible. Their stories could be told orally (perhaps on to tape), in pictures, in words or a combination of pictures and words.
Special colour The children could make the background using crayons, paint, collage, pastels or a combination of these. Which would be the most effective? Why? What other examples of camouflage are there?
Eyes tell a story Talk about the different parts of the eye. Let the children examine each other's eyes to note different shapes and colours. Discuss emotions and how they are shown other than on the face.
Creating harmony Before starting to colour the sheet, the children should name and identify the rainbow colours: red, orange, yellow, green, blue, indigo, violet. For accurate references, they should use science or art information books.
Weather report When the children have made their charts, they could use them daily over a period of time. Encourage them to build up a data record and ask their own questions. For example, on how many days was it raining? How many Mondays were cloudy?
Mirror, mirror Use small mirrors for this activity. Look at pictures in the mirror. What happens?
Ways of creating Ideally, the children should closely observe a real tree, using both sight and touch. If this is not possible, photographs or pictures of different trees can be used.
Butterfly life cycle With younger children, a good starting point for this activity would be to share with them Eric Carle's 'The Very Hungry Caterpillar' (Picture Puffin; Hamish Hamilton).
Stop press! Provide some newspapers for the children to study. They could include a picture and caption in their press reports. What is the difference between a headline and a caption?
Symbols Other possibilities might include: weather symbols, washing symbols and symbols from other alphabets.
Roman numerals The children could make up their own questions for others to answer.
What's the clue? Can the children identify the literary sources of the giants and other words? Jack and the Beanstalk; David and Goliath; Greek mythology; The Valiant Little Tailor - the Brothers Grimm (seven at one blow).
Make a map The children could put letter symbols along the bottom and numbers up the righthand side of their grid sheets. They could give grid references for the various locations or make up their own grid reference questions for others to answer.
Why write? Start by discussing the various purposes for writing. How many can the children think of? How many do they use? Where? When? Is writing always for communicating with other people? What about diaries, shopping lists? When using the chart, the children should circle or underline the two forms being compared.
Code wheel Discuss why codes are/were used, for example in wartime, and for spying. Are codes always secret? Discuss Morse and semaphore.The children will need to give a decoding instruction to enable their partners to crack the code, for example a=N.
Message carrier This activity is in two main stages: producing the coded message and devising a message carrier (a paper aeroplane, a car or similar wheeled object, a pulley system).
Light signals The list could include: TV, mirrors, flashing a torch in the dark, use of car headlights, bonfire beacons, devotional symbolic meaning in worship or celebrations (candles, divas), traffic signals, advertisements (flashing neon signs).
Tudor shop sign What shops were there in Tudor times? Use history books about the period as background reference. Not all shops sold articles; some performed a service, such as barbers. Finished signs could be hung across the room on string or a whole street scene might be designed to incorporate the signs. Remember, signs were generally double-sided and hung at right angles to shop fronts.
Signs and symbols Start by talking about the advantages of using pictorial symbols; universal understanding for example. How many examples can the children think of? They could collect pictures of examples for a class display.
Nursery rhyme tape You will need a selection of nursery rhyme books for the children to search through. In groups, they should make a list of possible material for inclusion. How will they make their final selection? How will they time their presentation? Empty tape boxes and examples of tape card inserts will be needed for the second part of the activity.
Make do and mend Use reference books about World War II. The children could interview people who can remember everyday life. Discuss what mass media was available at the time. They should select one medium for their campaign, then make a presentation to the rest of the class.

Journeys

Types of travel The children could fill in an individual sheet and then move around the class doing the research.
Round and round When the children have fixed the wheels on to the bus, using some form of split pin, discuss the information which needs to appear on the front of a bus.

Fire! Fire! The children could make a ladder either from card or straws. They should be encouraged to make it an extending ladder.
Pull the coaches It is best to build the model with wheels that are fixed to the axles rather than wheels that turn freely. Elastic bands can then be fixed to an axle to power it.
A flat tyre The children could write a story about the day the tyre deflated.
Design a sail pattern This activity is best carried out after children have investigated the Vikings. Some research about longships would indicate appropriate sail designs.
Journey into space If the children do not suggest it, introduce the idea of planets that are not spherical. When making a three-dimensional model, chicken wire is an ideal base. It takes papier mâché strips well and is easily fixed to a wooden base with staples.
Seafarer's alphabet Encourage the children to choose two or three of the listed objects and investigate, in detail, how they are made.
Meshing cogs In tackling this worksheet, children will need access to some form of cog system. If manufactured ones are not available, they can be constructed from cheese wedge boxes and corrugated card.
Ice-cream island Encourage the children to discuss their ideas and to make an outline of page headings and contents on the flat plan (see notes on general sheets for using a flat plan). They should try out ideas and make amendments until a final version is reached.
Going by train Encourage the children to make their own timetables.
Planning a Roman road Encourage the children to investigate how a Roman road was constructed. They can then make a three-dimensional model of the layout.
Safety first Let the children draft and re-draft their plans before making their final booklets.
A milestone Milestones are best made from clay as it can be moulded easily, written on, amended if necessary, painted or glazed and eventually used as a paperweight or an ornament. The children will need to research appropriate inscriptions for their milestones.
Voyage of exploration These maps make effective displays when enlarged and mounted on cartridge paper. Find examples of a Gothic or italic alphabet for the children to copy.
Finding the way Use stiff card, felt pens and Blu-tack for this activity. Discuss clear lettering, contrasting and dominant colours, sign height and the problems of outdoor signs.
Garage forecourt When the plan is complete the children could make a three-dimensional model of the garage or a display board giving information, such as the price of petrol.
Cut down on cars If the class has access to video recording equipment, the children could plan a television campaign.
Narrow-boat living space Go on to make scaled models, perhaps using matchboxes inside a large 'tin foil' box.
Evacuation Encourage the children to examine a map of the United Kingdom and ask them to discuss, then identify, the areas to which they think children might have been evacuated for safety during the war.
Move it! Investigate ways of lifting bricks to make a tall structure, such as a pyramid.

General sheets

Planning sheet Children can have a good concept of what a plan entails if they understand that one can be sent to the other side of the world and anyone reading it, and subsequently building the model, will build one identical to that which the designer constructed. The use of this sheet will vary depending upon the activity. For example, 'things to include' may not always be filled in, as in the Viking braid pattern activity on page 21 for which the sheet should just be used for designing, but may be useful for notes on accessories required for the Board game on page 42.
Testing sheet This sheet should be used to record the results of any tests carried out. For example, after the Oven glove activity on page 13 has been completed, the children might decide that they need to test it for fit, strength, protection from heat and flame resistance. They should list these at the top of the sheet and then name each of the tests and results and final evaluation below. Any such tests should be supervised by an adult.
Self-evaluation sheet It is vital that children are able to assess the success of the work that they have done and how they carried it out. More information on this is given on page 5.
Model figure template This sheet should be mounted on to card and the outline figure cut out. It can be used for designing clothes, such as Cinderella's ball gown on page 19, or a sports kit to bear the logo design as set out on page 31.
Flat plan This is a useful tool for planning the production of any written or designed work. All publishers use this tool when planning pages or stages of any production. The children should understand that it is not the final product and can be altered many times until their plan is satisfactory to them.
Grid paper This sheet of one-centimetre squares can be used for a variety of purposes, such as laying out houses, rooms, furniture or play parks like the one on page 41.

Name ____________________

Whose hat?

Here are eight different hats. Who would wear each one?

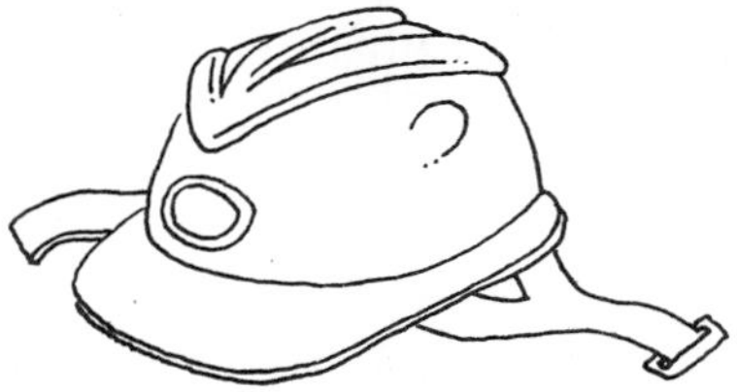

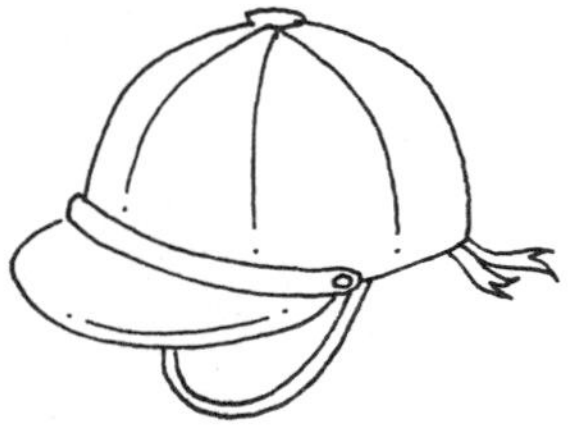

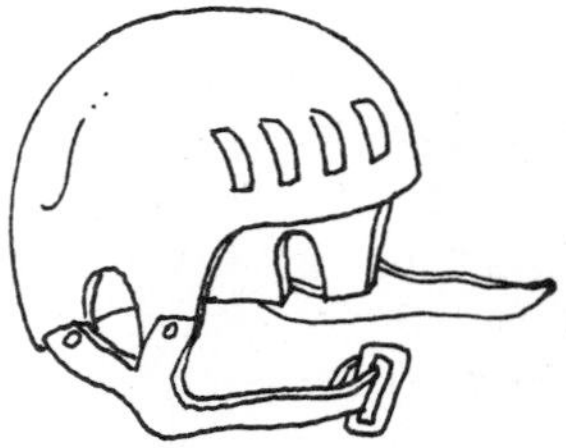

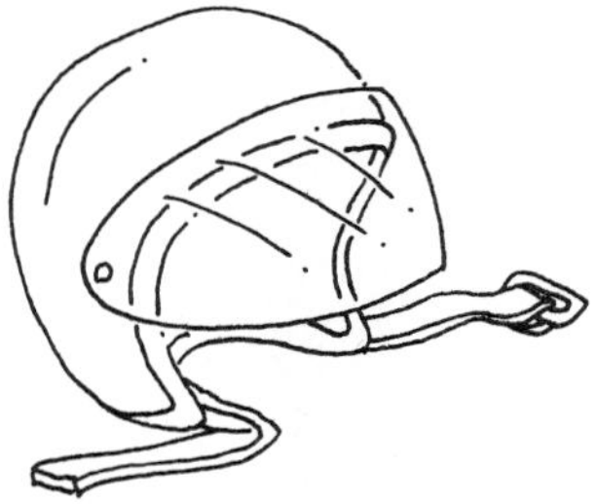

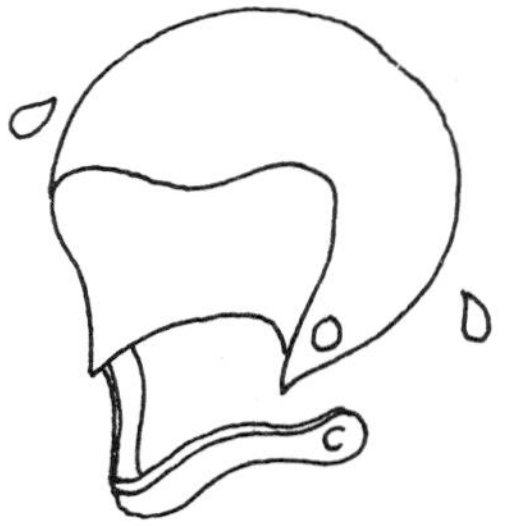

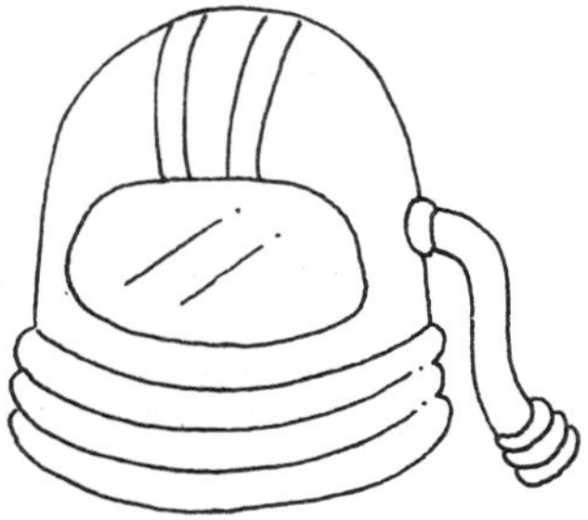

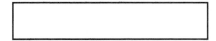

✤ Which one is the odd one out? ____

Why? ____

Name ____________________

Sun-glasses

My design

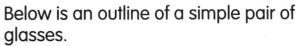

Below is an outline of a simple pair of glasses.

✤ Draw a rough design for fancy sun-glasses, using the outline as the basic shape.

✤ Transfer your design to the outline and colour it.

✤ Stick the outline on to cardboard. Cut out the front and sides and stick them together to make your glasses.

✤ How can you make tinted lenses?

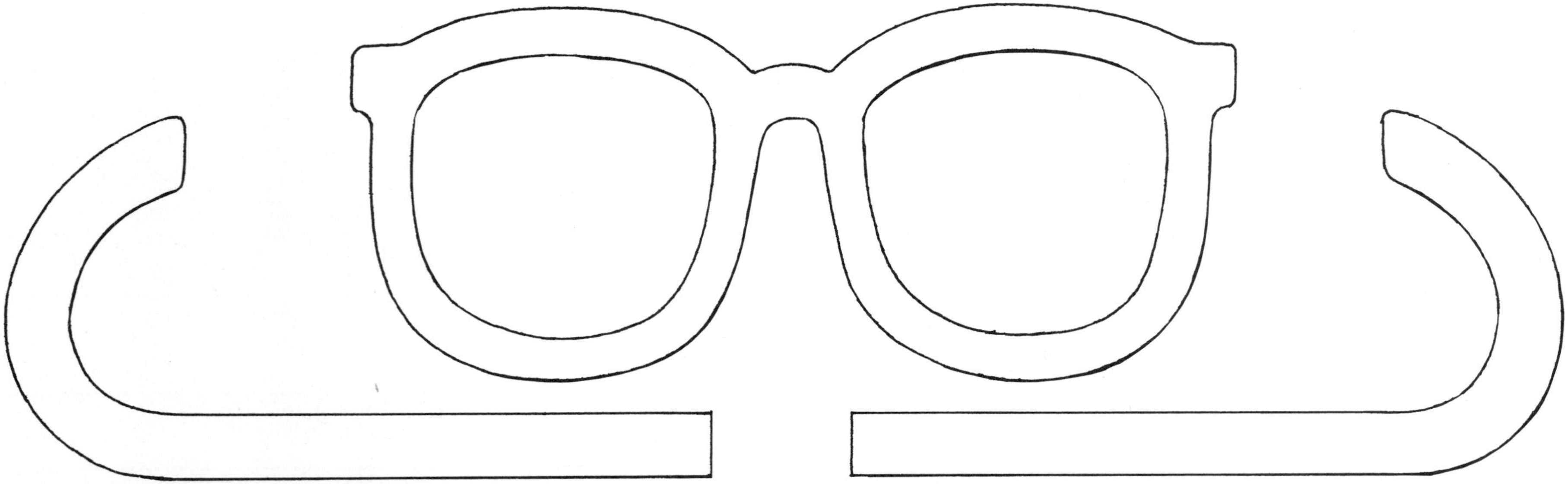

Name ____________________

Oven glove

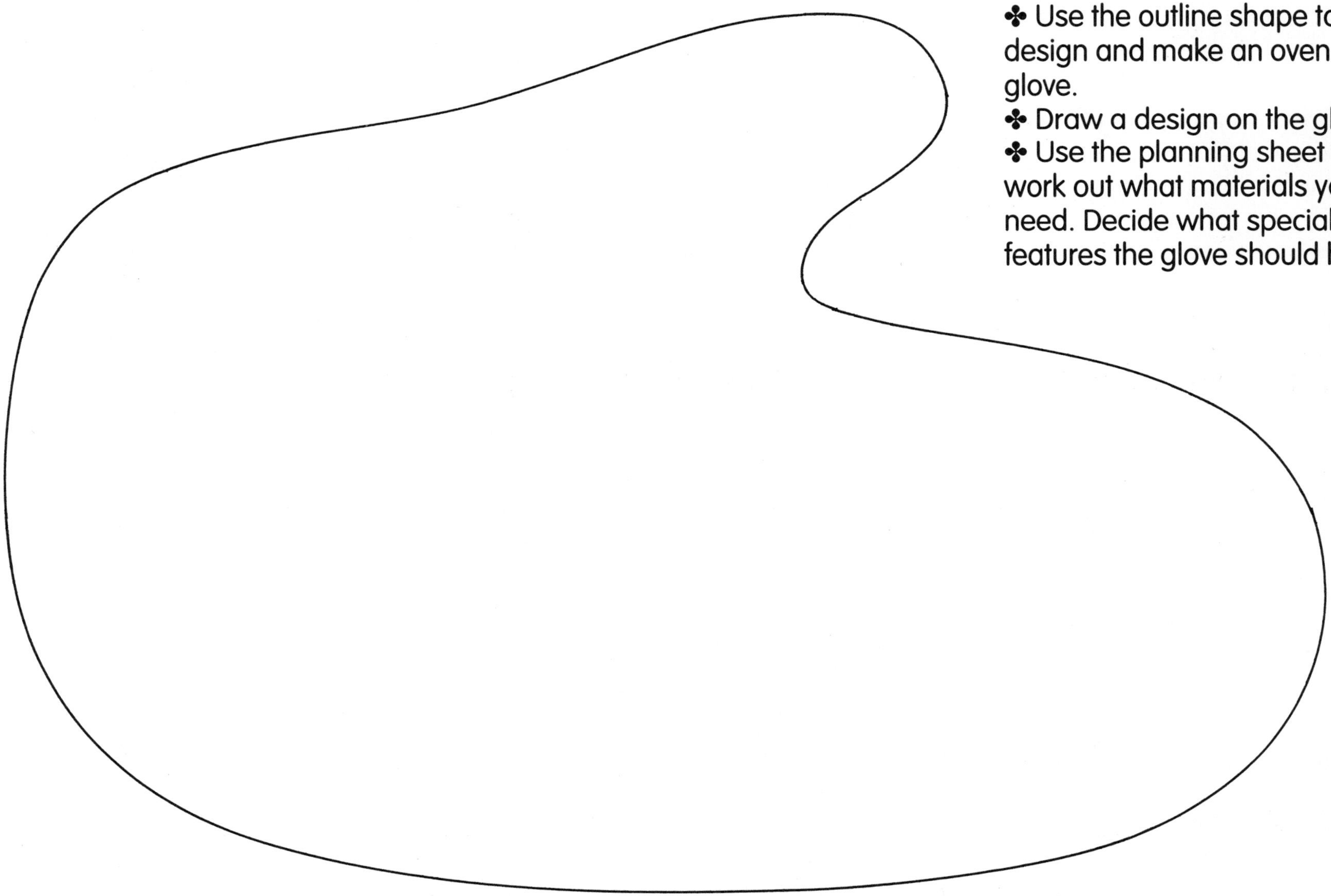

✤ Use the outline shape to design and make an oven glove.
✤ Draw a design on the glove.
✤ Use the planning sheet to work out what materials you will need. Decide what special features the glove should have.

Name ____________________

What will teddy wear?

What will teddy wear?

Here is a teddy with some clothes.

✤ How many ways can you find to dress the teddy using only two items of clothing?

✤ How many ways using three items of clothing?

✤ You can cut out teddy and the clothes to help you.

✤ How will you record your results?

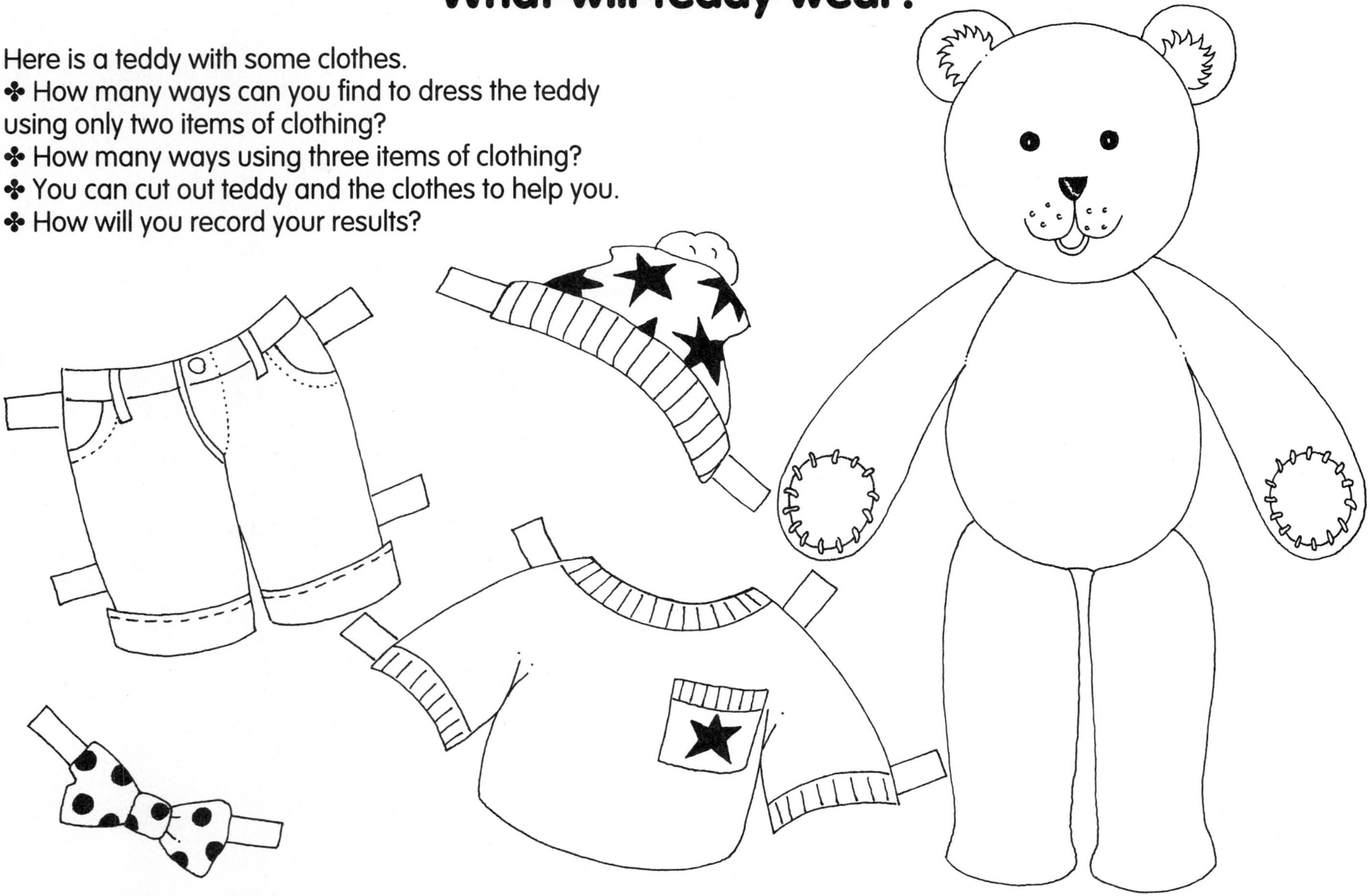

Masks

People throughout the world use masks for different occasions, especially celebrations.

✤ Using the planning sheet, design and make a mask for a particular celebration.

✤ The drawings on this page might give you some ideas.

✤ How will you make sure that your mask will fit you?

✤ How will you decorate it so that it is bright and easily seen?

✤ How will you fix it to your face?

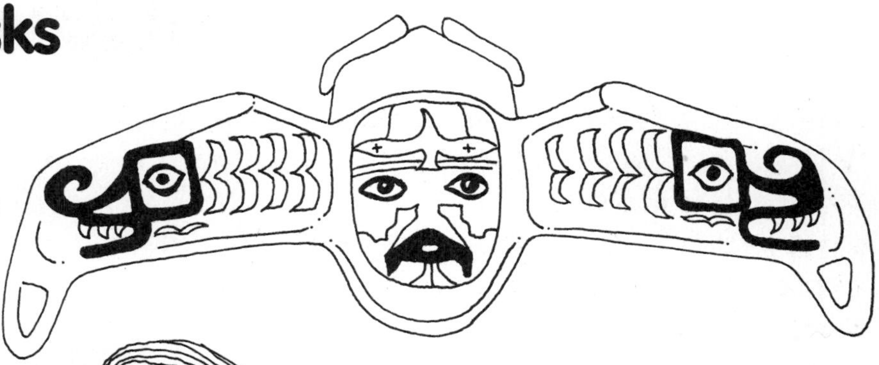

Name ____________________

Modern jewellery

Your class has been put in charge of the jewellery stall for your school fair.

✤ Use these basic shapes for:
- a pair of earings
- a pendant
- a brooch
- a ring

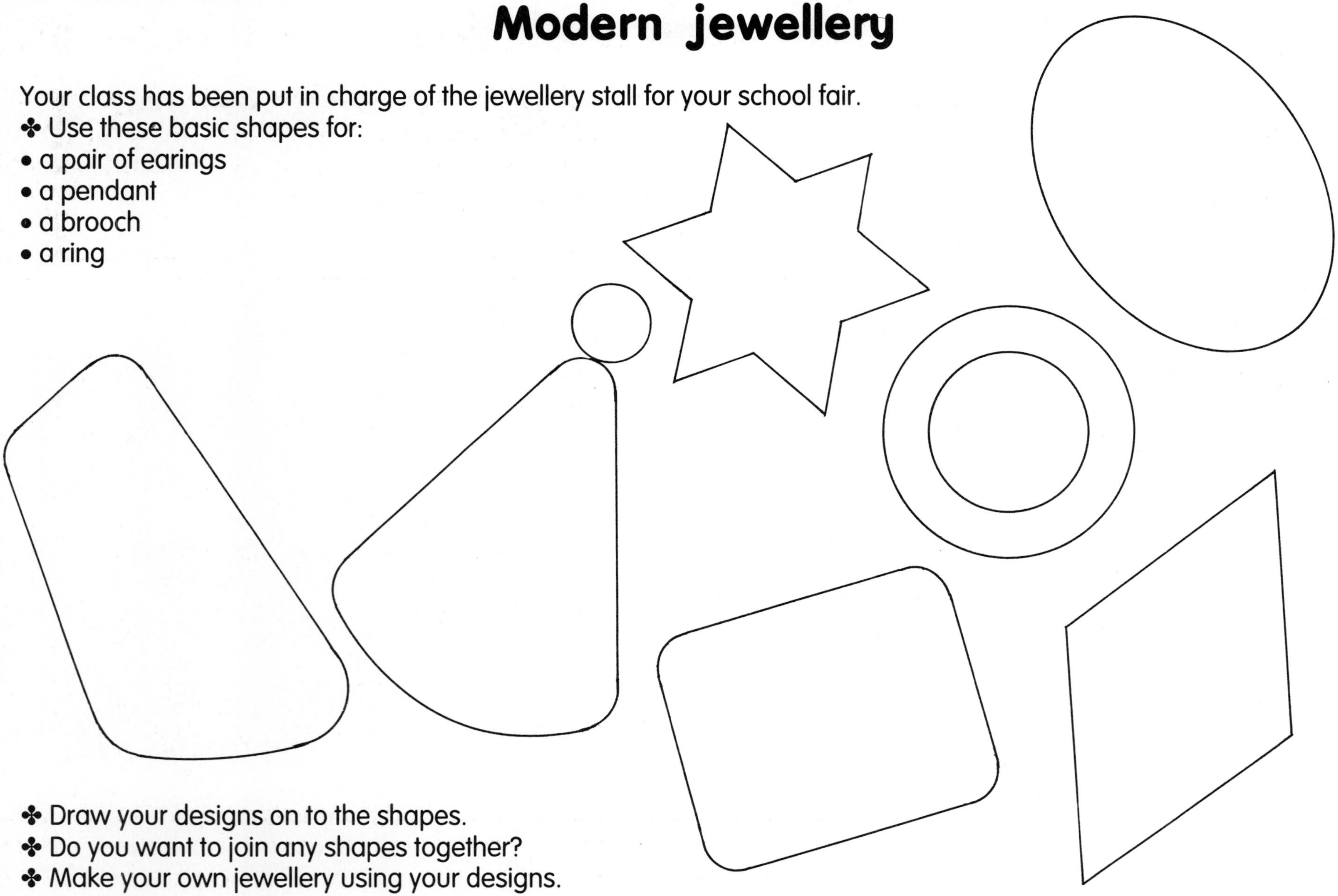

✤ Draw your designs on to the shapes.
✤ Do you want to join any shapes together?
✤ Make your own jewellery using your designs.

Border design

This is a mango pattern shape. It is a traditional Indian design often used on sari borders, bedcovers, dress material and many other things.

✤ Complete this border design. Use three colours to decorate your border.

✤ Try sewing a border using your completed design.

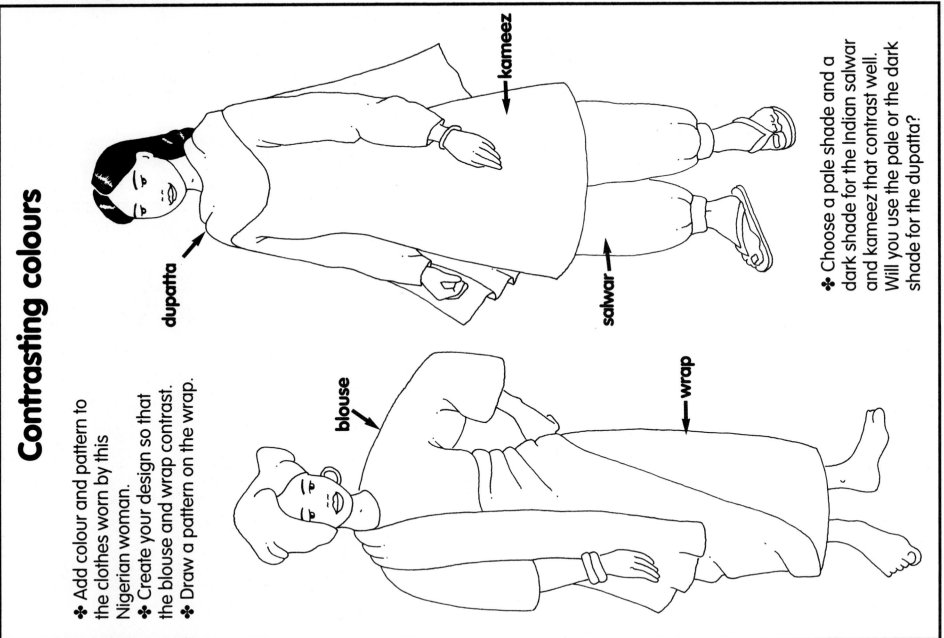

Contrasting colours

✤ Add colour and pattern to the clothes worn by this Nigerian woman.
✤ Create your design so that the blouse and wrap contrast.
✤ Draw a pattern on the wrap.

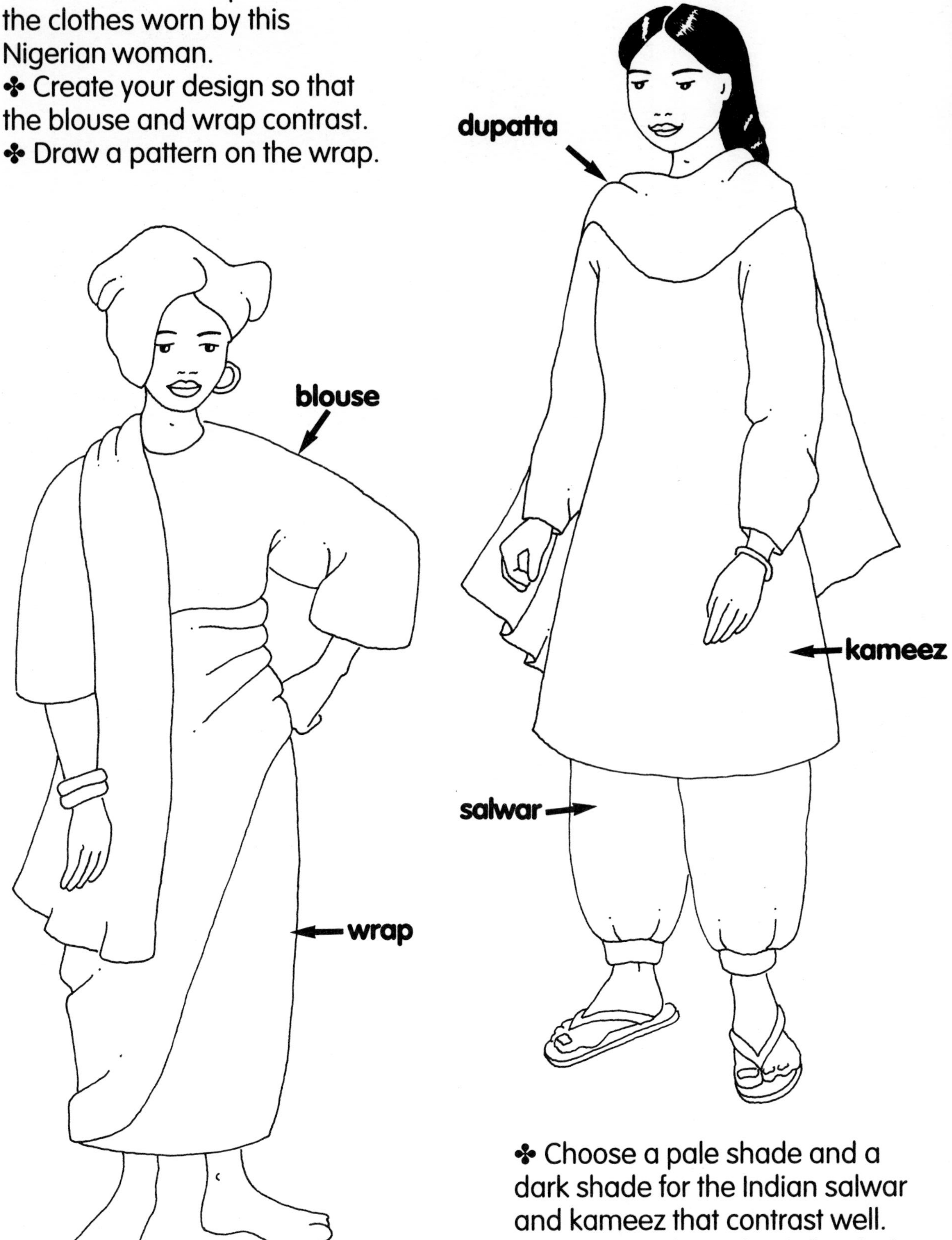

✤ Choose a pale shade and a dark shade for the Indian salwar and kameez that contrast well. Will you use the pale or the dark shade for the dupatta?

Name ____________________

Cinderella's ball dress

Sketch pad

✤ Design and make a beautiful dress for Cinderella to wear to the ball.
✤ Sketch some ideas for the design on this sheet.
✤ Choose one to make.
✤ Use the planning sheet and the model figure template to help you.

Name ____________________

Market stalls

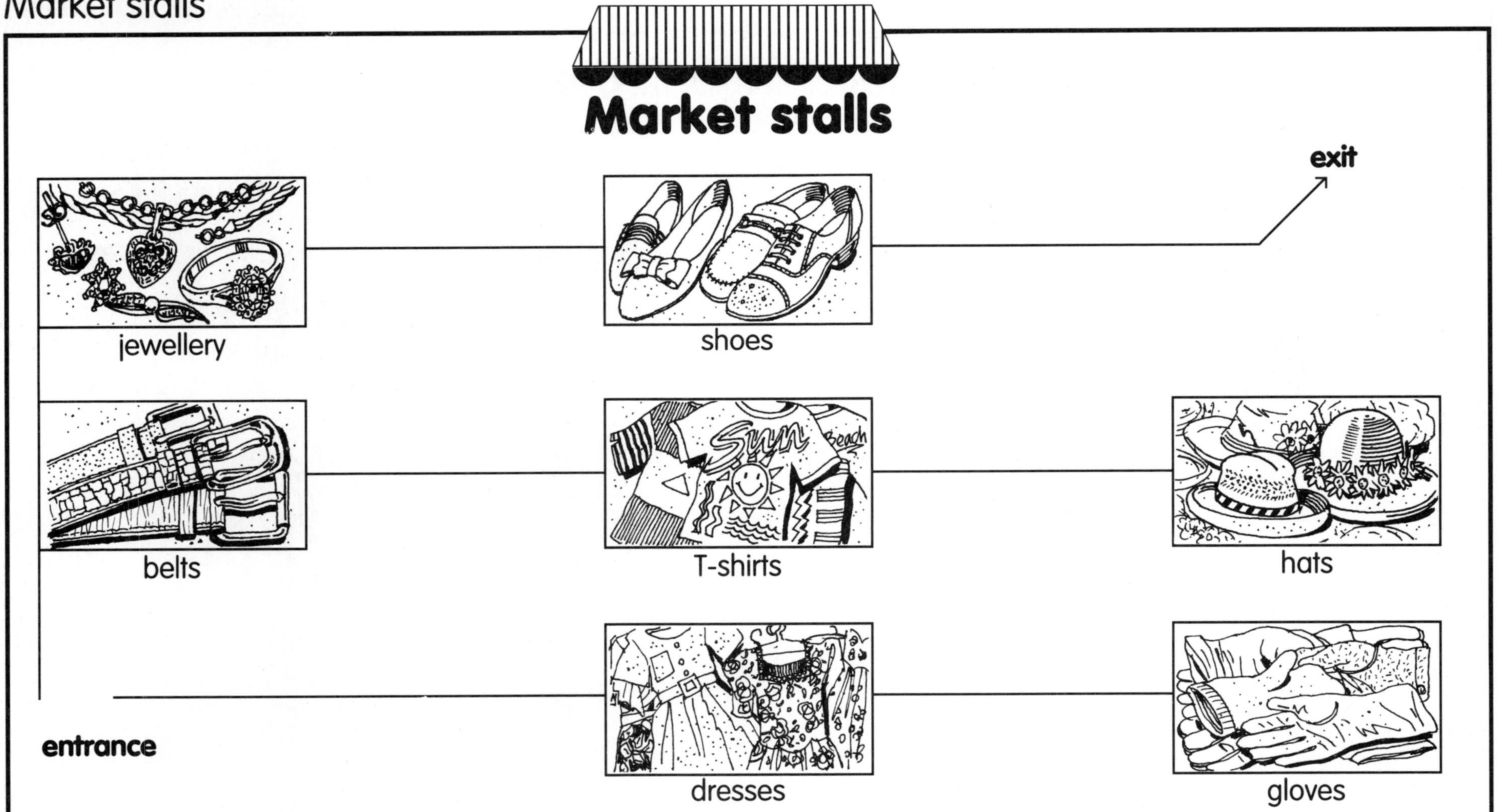

You are visiting the clothes section of a market.

- Start at the entrance and leave at the exit.
- Look for as many routes as possible to visit each stall only once.
- Never go across a line more than once.
- Think of a way to record your results.

Name ____________________

Viking braid pattern

The Viking people often dressed in woolly clothing. These clothes were woven at home by the women. The men wore tunics that were often decorated with braid.

✤ Use the planning sheet to design a woven pattern for the braid around the neck, hem and cuffs of this Viking tunic.

✤ Draw your design on the tunic below.

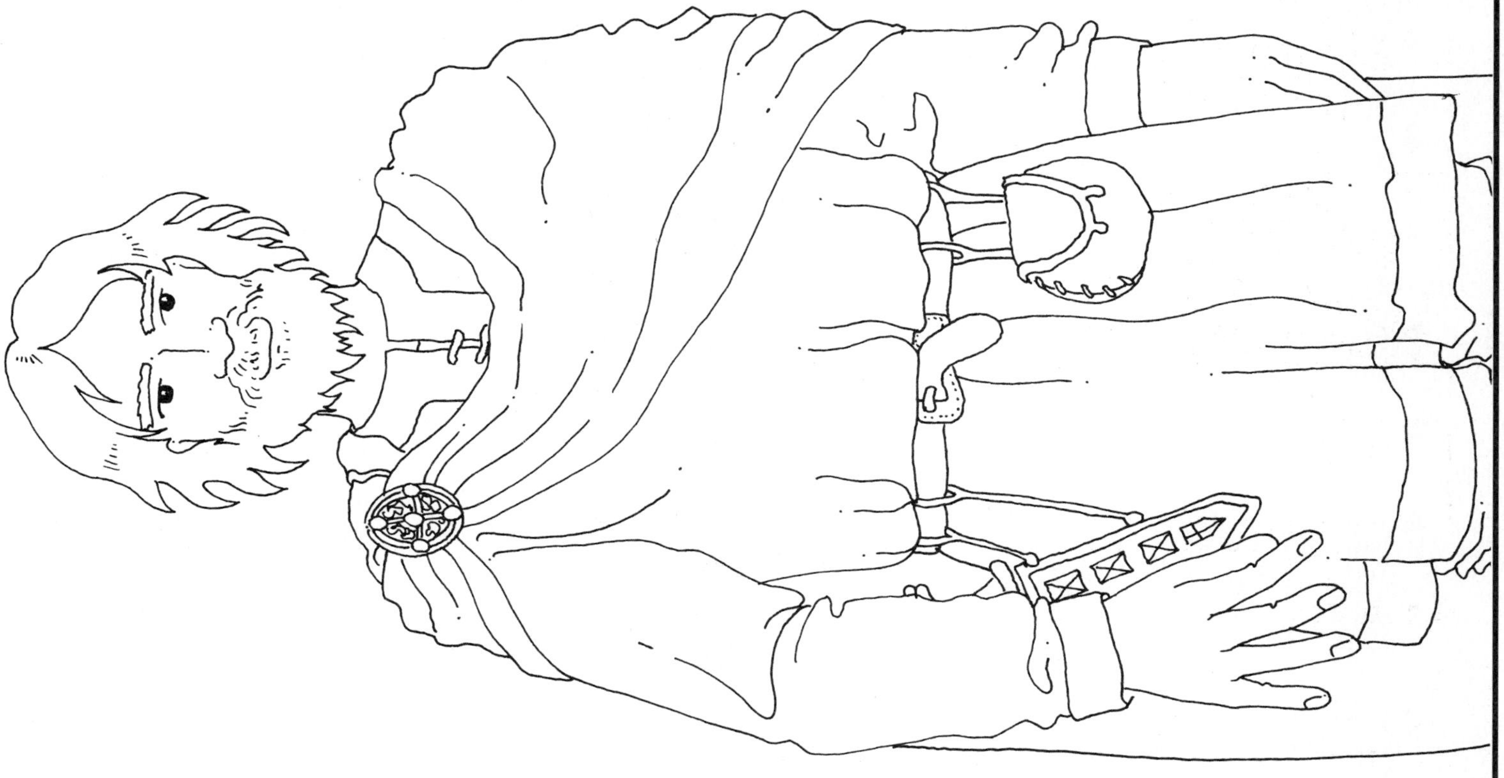

Name ____________________

Coordinate clothes

Coordinate clothes

✤ What clothing can you find at each coordinate? Remember to read the letter axis first.

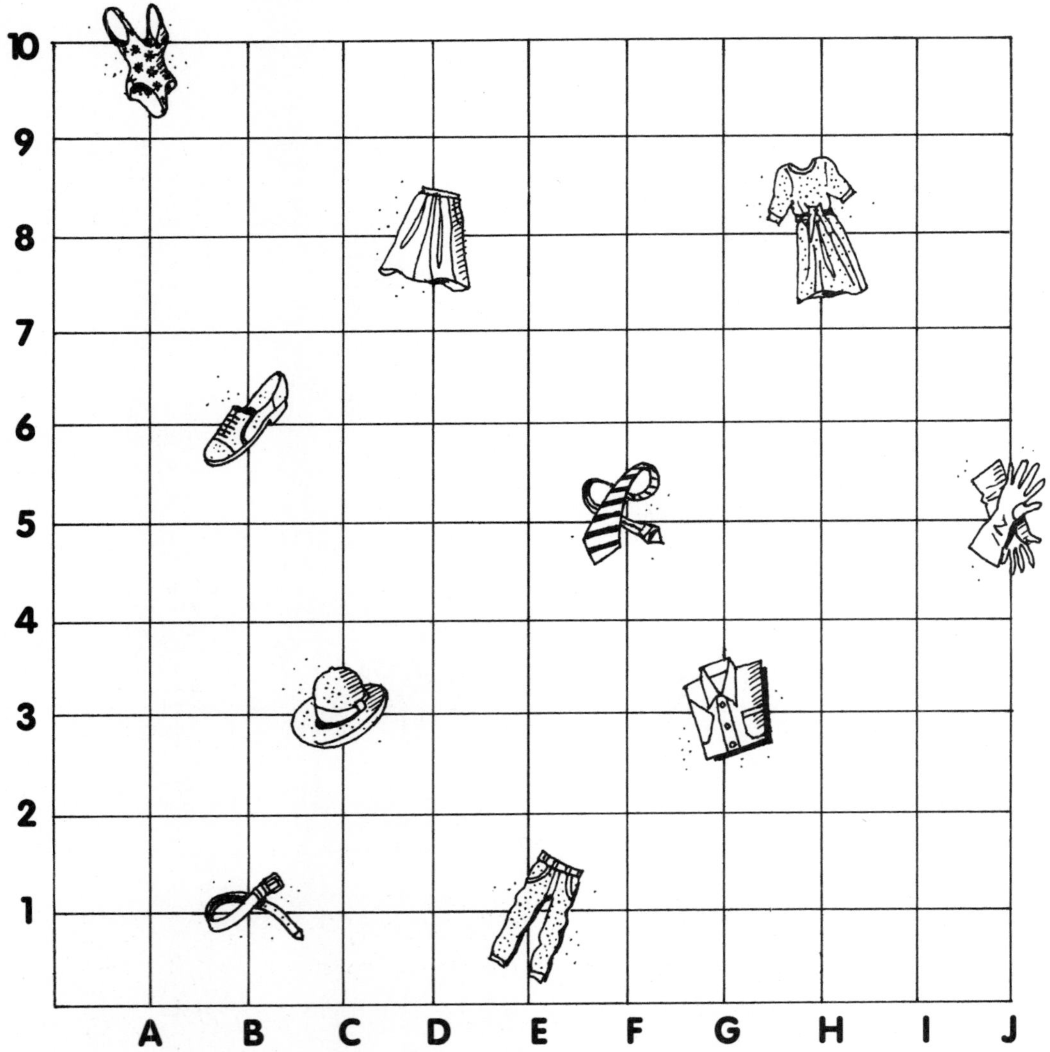

B1 ____________________

E1 ____________________

C3 ____________________

B6 ____________________

J5 ____________________

F5 ____________________

H8 ____________________

D8 ____________________

G3 ____________________

A10 ____________________

✤ Use grid paper to make up your own coordinate clothes grid. Try it on a friend.

Name ____________________

Fasten it!

There are many ways of fastening clothes.

- ✤ Look at the pictures below. None of the clothes have fastenings.
- ✤ Design a good fastener for each item and draw it in.
- ✤ Label the type of fastener you have chosen.

____

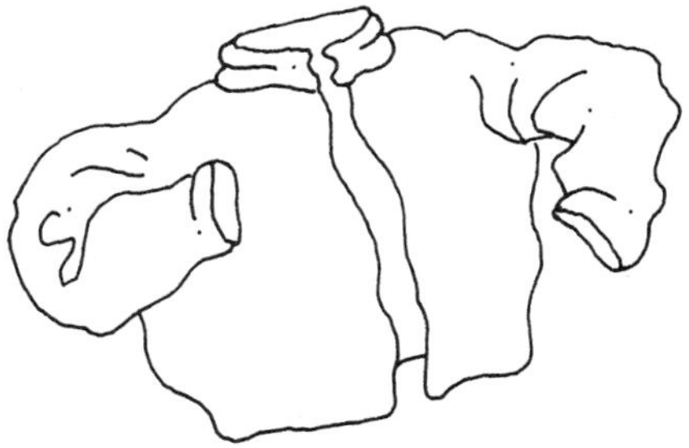

____

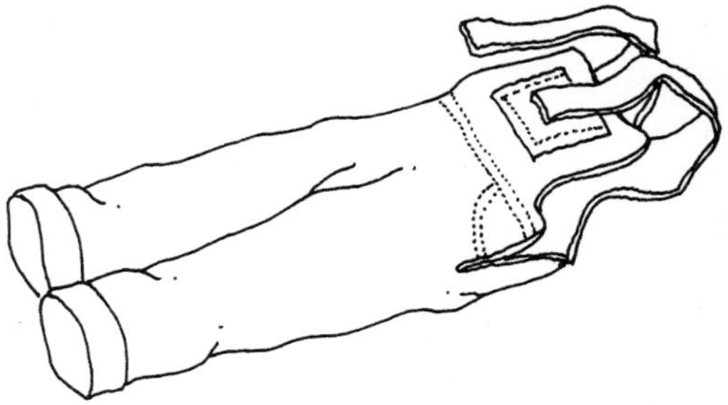

____

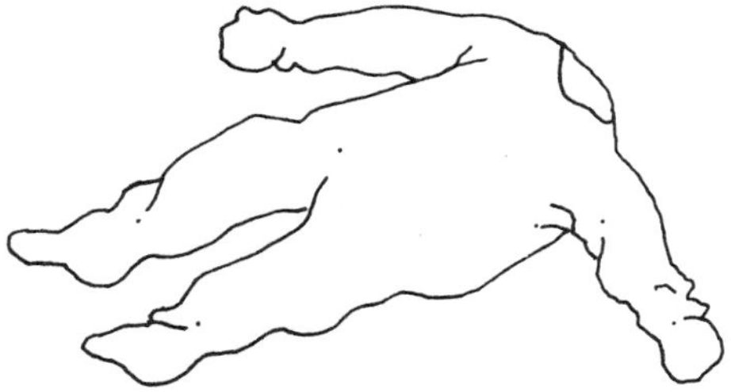

____

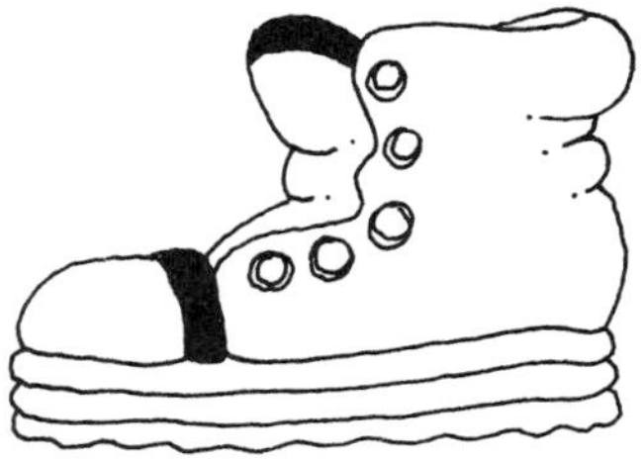

____

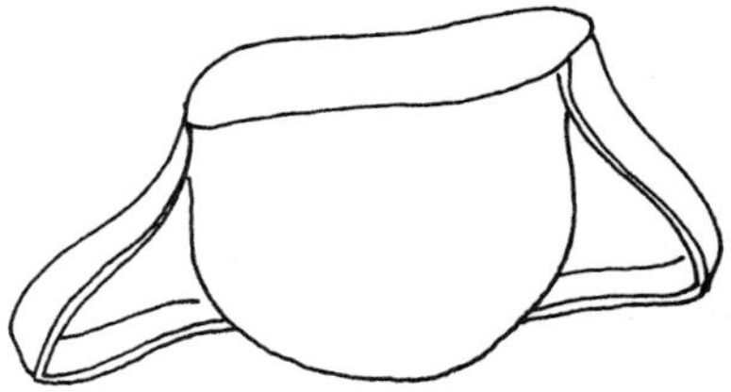

____

✤ Choose from these fastenings:
zip, Velcro, buckles, toggles, laces, hooks/eyes, poppers, buttons/holes, loops/buttons, drawstring.

Name ____________________

Fancy dress

Fancy dress

My design

You are going to a fancy dress party but have no money to make an expensive costume. You have to make a costume using the materials shown below.

✤ Draw your design in the box and label it to show what you have used. How will you fix the materials together?

Name ____________________

Think again!

People often throw clothes away rather than mend or alter them.

- ✤ How could you recycle the clothes shown below?
- ✤ Draw your design in the space by each item.

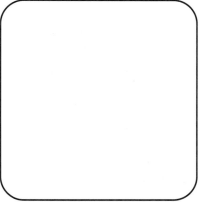

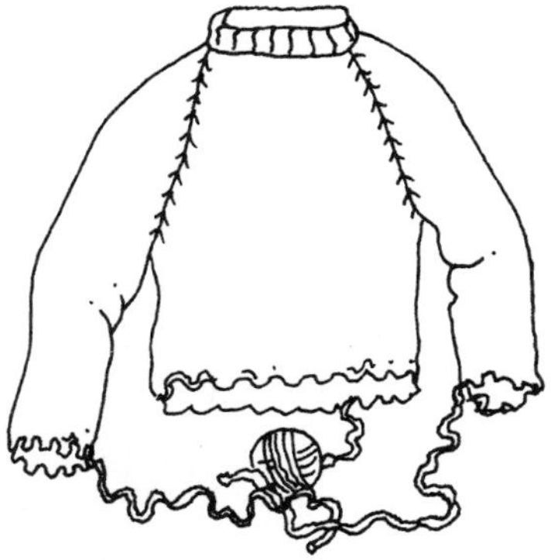

Name ______________________

Desert island shoes

Desert island shoes

Imagine you are stranded on a desert island without any shoes.

- Using the natural materials you find on the island, design and make a pair of shoes to protect your feet when you go exploring.
- On the sheet below, list the materials you could use.
- How long will your shoes last?
- Draw and label your design.

List

____

____

____

____

____

____

____

____

____

____

My design

Time capsule clothes

✤ Imagine you are going to bury a time capsule in your school playground. Its contents should show people in the year 2095 the type of clothes typically worn by children in the 1990s.
✤ What ten items of clothing would you choose?
✤ Work with a partner. Write your list on this sheet and give reasons why you chose each item.

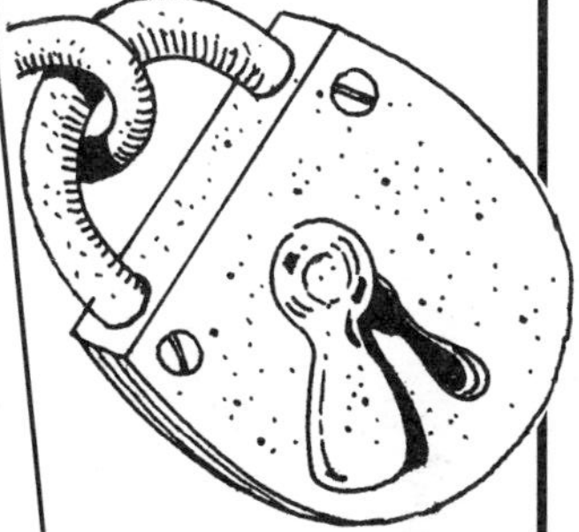

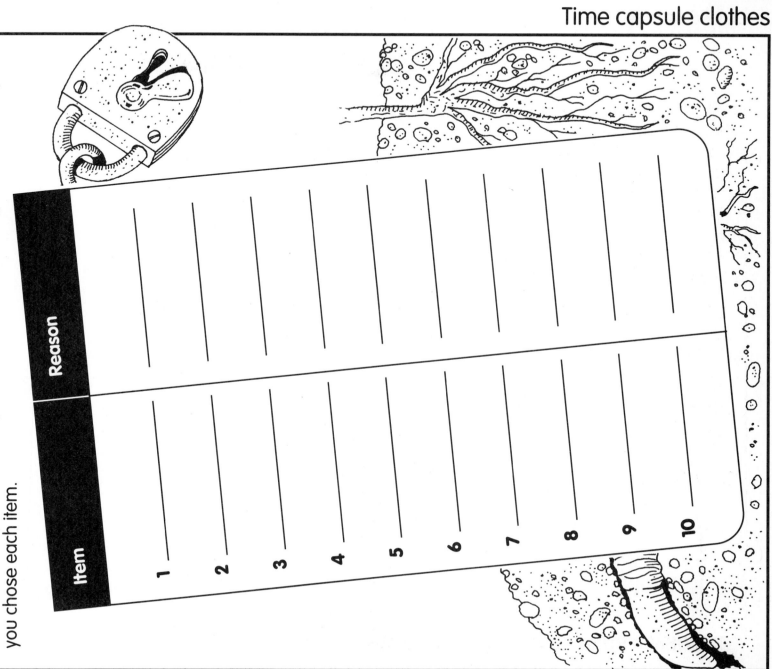

Item	Reason
1 ____________	____________
2 ____________	____________
3 ____________	____________
4 ____________	____________
5 ____________	____________
6 ____________	____________
7 ____________	____________
8 ____________	____________
9 ____________	____________
10 ____________	____________

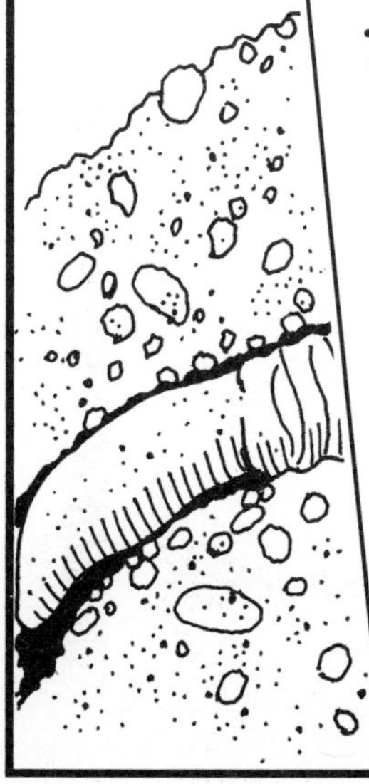

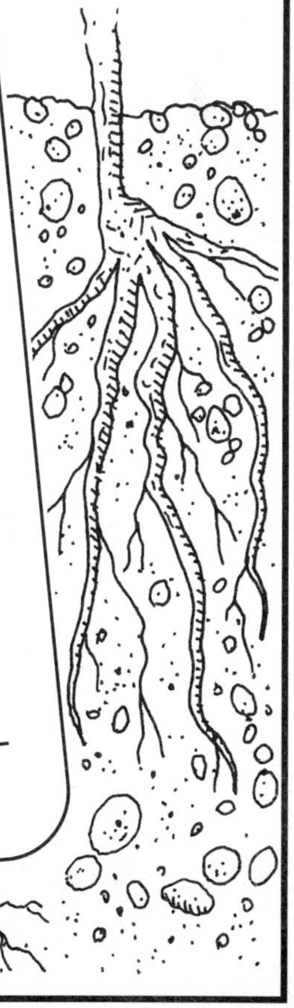

Name ____________________

School uniform

School uniform

✤ What are the advantages and disadvantages of a school uniform?

Advantages	Disadvantages

✤ Design a uniform for your school. List the important features you would include.

Important features

✤ You could use the model figure template to try out your designs.

Caretaker's overall

A school caretaker's work is sometimes dirty and messy. He needs something to wear to protect his clothes.

✤ What would be the best type of material for an overall?

✤ List some materials to test for wear and tear, waterproofing and crease resistance. Record your tests here.

✤ What else could you test for?

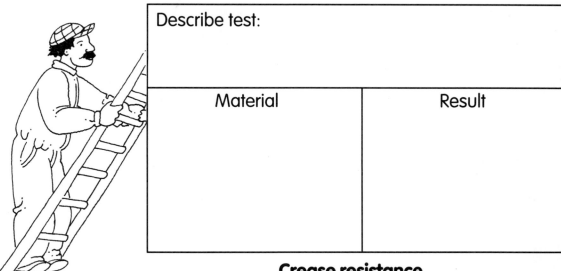

Wear and tear

Describe test:	
Material	Result

Waterproofing

Describe test:	
Material	Result

Crease resistance

Describe test:	
Material	Result

Name ____________________

Panjunglia

Panjunglia

Indian women often wear panjunglia on special occasions.

✤ A panjunglia is made up of a bracelet, a disc in the centre of the back of the hand and some rings joined together by decorative chains.

✤ Design a panjunglia using the hand shape below.

Name ____________________

Sports kit logo

✤ Design a logo for your school sports kit.

✤ Use the strip at the bottom of the page to test out colour combinations. Colour each square a different colour and cut them out.

✤ Using the model figure template, design a sports kit with your logo on it.

✤ Draw your finished logo on this shirt.

My design

Name ____________

Choose a wardrobe

You have been given a clothes allowance of £80.
✤ Choose your summer wardrobe from this catalogue page.
Be careful to mark the right size.

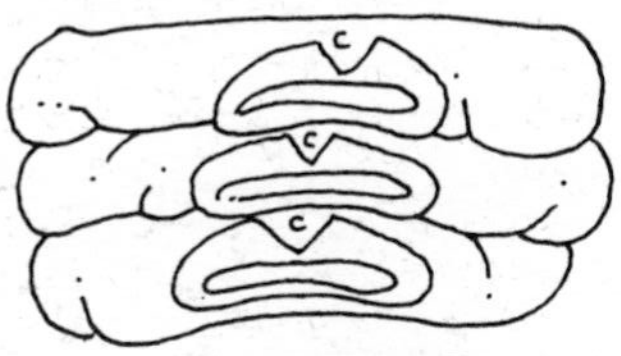

Polo T-shirt
Ages 5/6 *£5.99*
Ages 7/8 *£5.99*
Ages 9/10 *£5.99*
Ages 11/12 *£5.99*
State size ____________

Patterned T-shirt
Up to age 8 *£4.99*
Ages 8-11 *£5.99*
State size ____________

Plain T-shirt
Up to age 8 *£4.00*
Age 8 plus *£5.00*
State size ____________

Crew neck acrylic sweater
Up to age 8 *£13.99*
Ages 8-10 *£14.99*
Age 10 plus *£15.99*
State size ____________

Denim skirt
Up to age 8 *£7.99*
Age 8 plus *£8.99*
State size ____________

Denim jeans
Up to age 8 *£11.99*
Age 8 plus *£12.99*
State size ____________

Shorts
Up to age 8 *£6.99*
Age 8 plus *£7.99*
State size ____________

White trousers
Up to age 8 *£10.99*
Age 8 plus *£11.99*
State size ____________

Bomber jacket
Up to age 8 *£20.00*
Age 8 plus *£22.00*
Colours - black, yellow
State size/colour ____________
____

Trainers
All sizes *25.00*
State size ____________

Sandals
Up to size13*£12.99*
Sizes 1 - 5 *£14.99*
Colours - tan, black, white, navy
State size/colour ____________
____

Total spent ____________
Post free on orders more than £50
Name ____________
Address ____________
____
____________ Postcode ____________
Your order may take up to 14 days.

Puzzle pieces

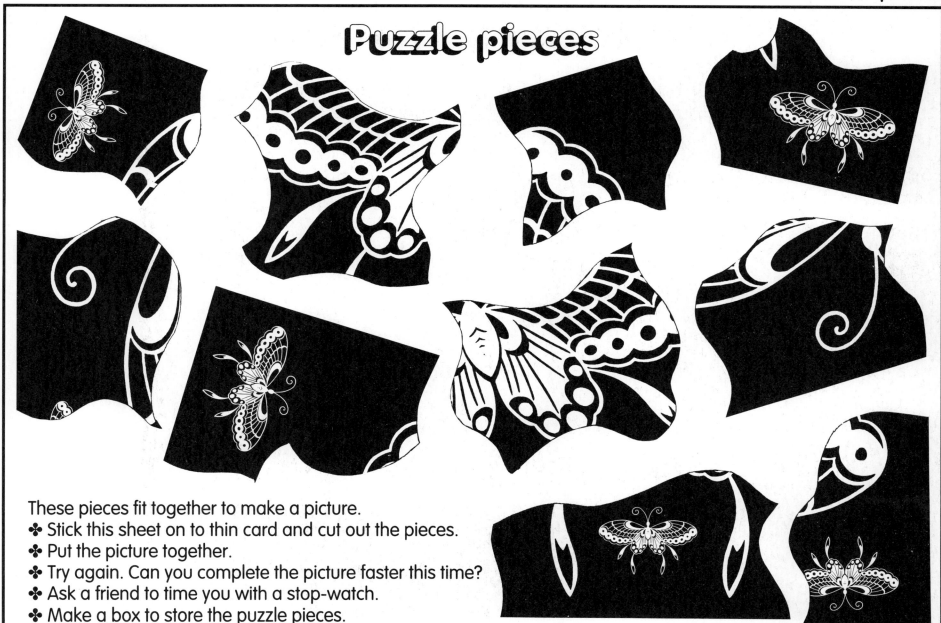

These pieces fit together to make a picture.

- ✤ Stick this sheet on to thin card and cut out the pieces.
- ✤ Put the picture together.
- ✤ Try again. Can you complete the picture faster this time?
- ✤ Ask a friend to time you with a stop-watch.
- ✤ Make a box to store the puzzle pieces.

Mirror monster fun

- ✤ Use a mirror to give this dragon a twin.
- ✤ Can you make them rub noses?
- ✤ Make their tails touch.
- ✤ Make one balance on top of the other.
- ✤ Make both dragons disappear.
- ✤ Record what you do.

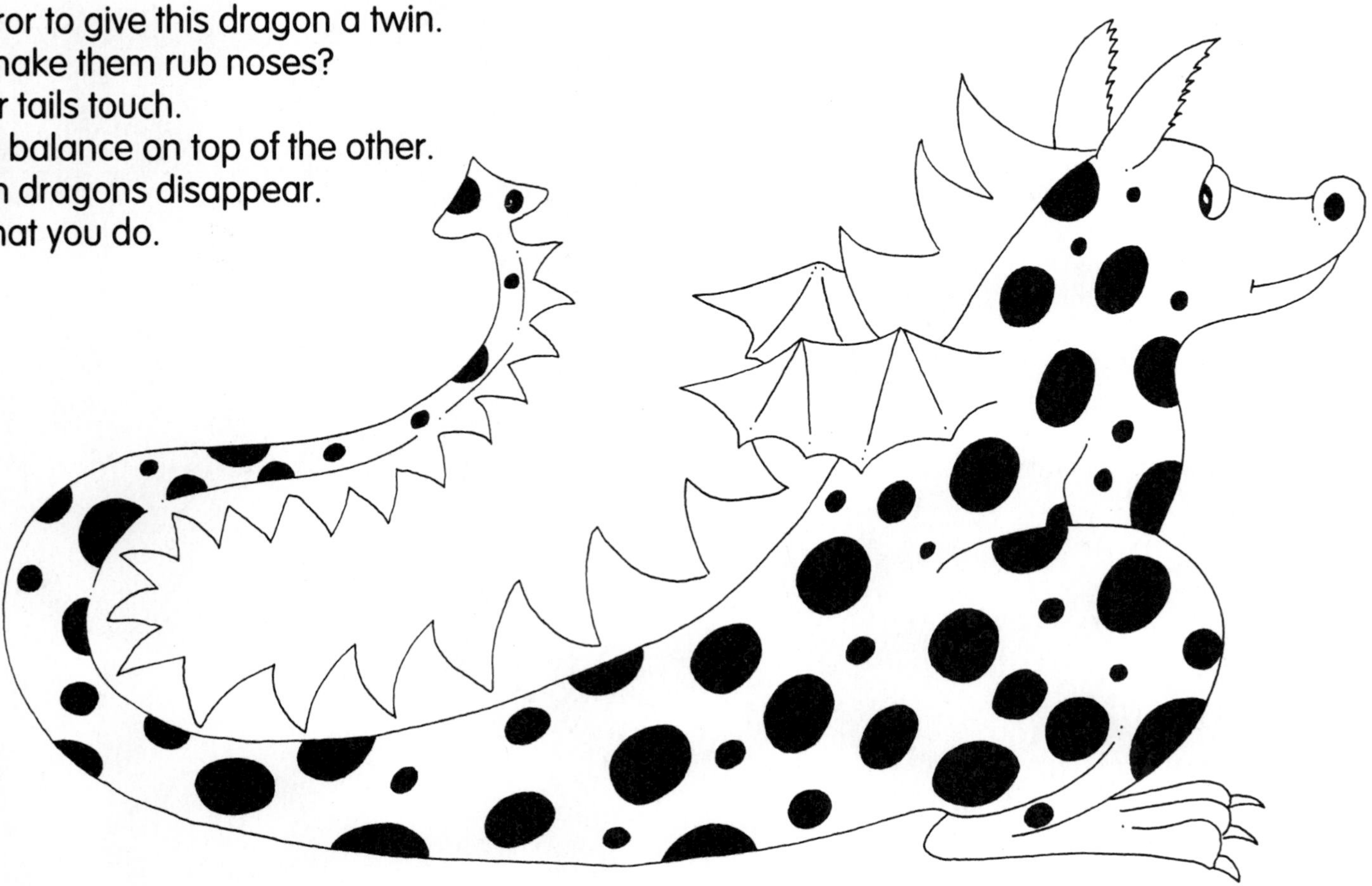

- ✤ Think of some more mirror tricks for the dragons.

Puppet Show

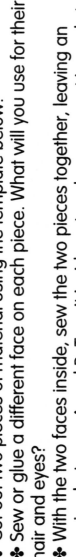

- Cut out two pieces of material using the template below.
- Sew or glue a different face on each piece. What will you use for their hair and eyes?
- With the two faces inside, sew the two pieces together, leaving an opening between A and B. Turn it inside out and your puppet is ready to use.
- Make up a simple play using your two characters.

Invent a game

- ✤ Glue these pairs of pictures and the blank card on to cardboard.
- ✤ Cut out each pair.
- ✤ Invent a game using the cards.
- ✤ Write the rules for your game.

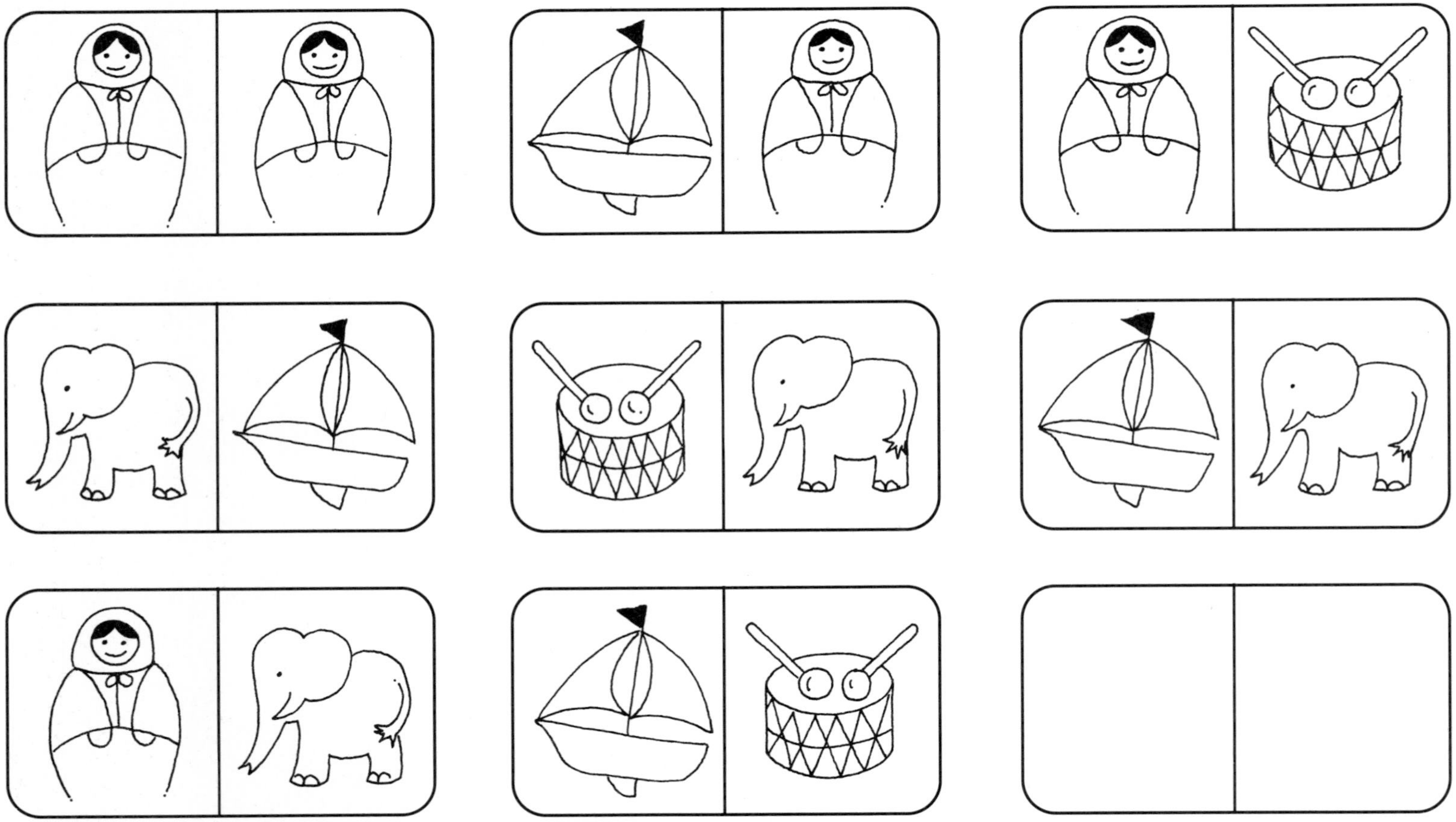

Name ____________________

Balancing toy

Balancing toy

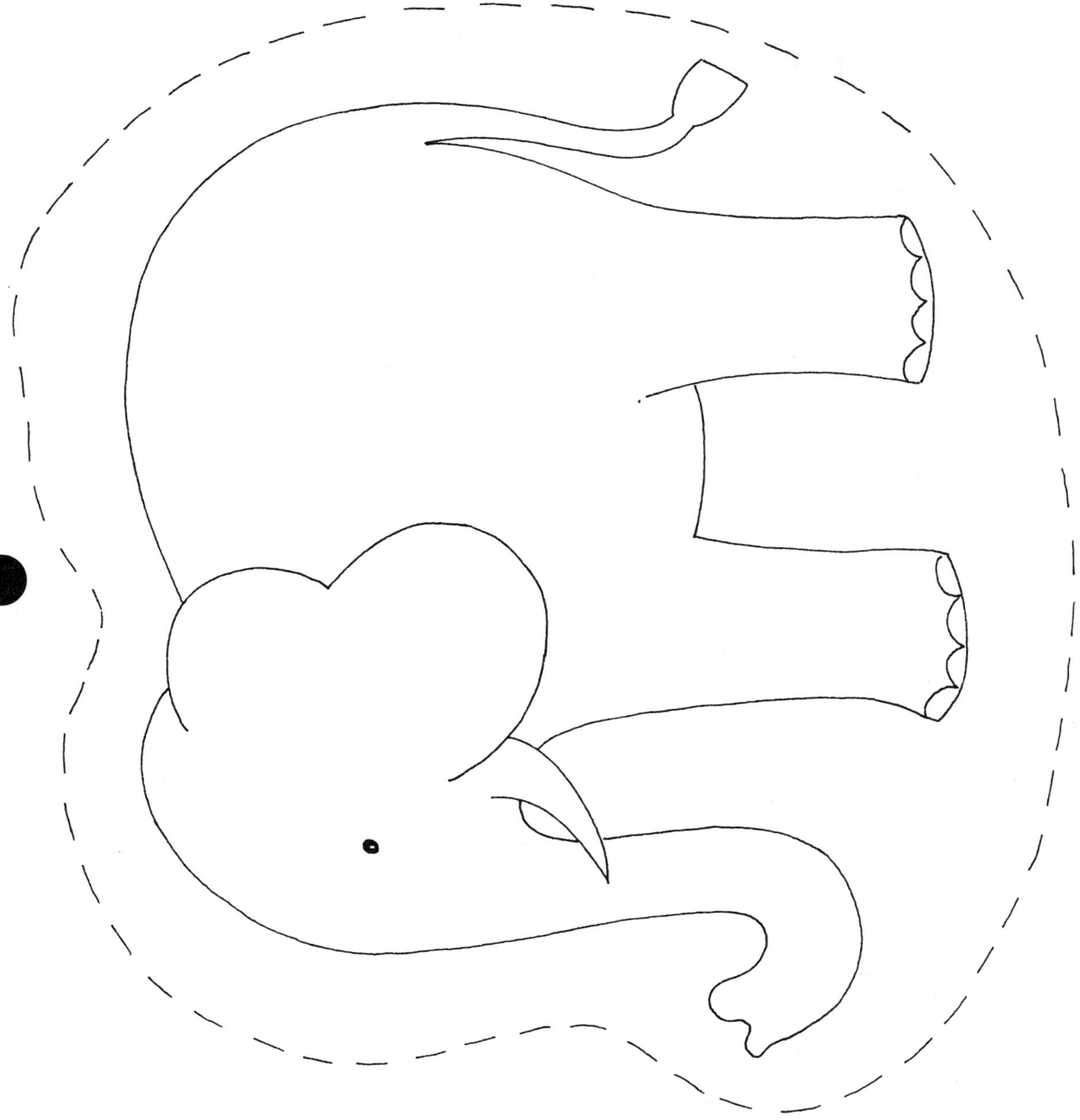

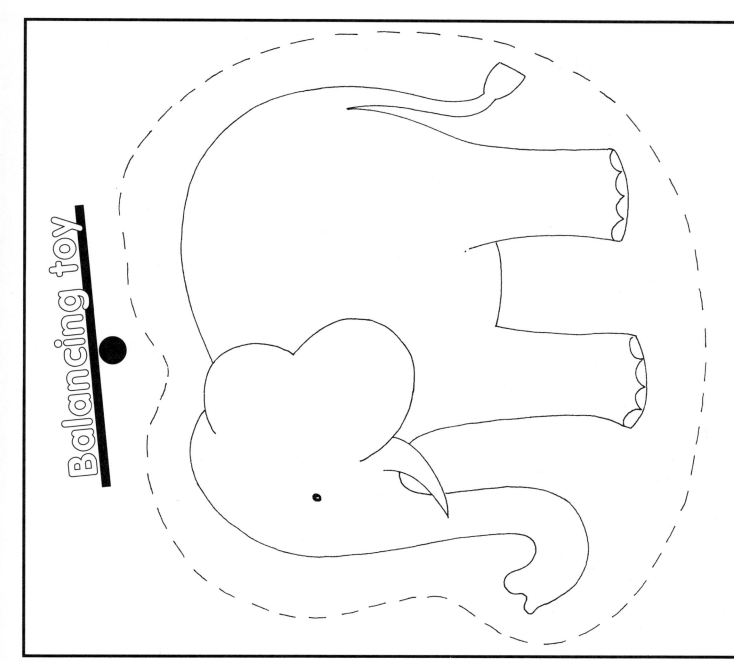

- ✤ Cut round the dotted line and stick the picture on to strong card.
- ✤ When it is dry, cut out the elephant.
- ✤ Stretch a piece of string tightly between two desks.
- ✤ Add weights made from Plasticine to the elephant to make it balance on your tightrope.
- ✤ Can you make a balancing toy of your own? It need not balance on a tightrope; you could make it balance on the edge of a table or the back of a chair.
- ✤ Use the planning sheet to work out your design.

Name ______________

Holiday camp

Holiday camp

These signs were used at a holiday camp to show what facilities were available.

✤ Under each sign write what you think it means.

✤ In these boxes design a sign for:

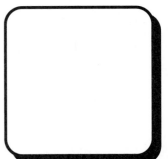

- tennis
- pony trekking
- disco

Name ____________________

Bouncy bat

✤ Cut out these three shapes and glue them together to make a bat.
✤ Can you make its wings flap?
✤ Make the bat into a bouncy toy.
(Hint: elastic bands, paper-clips and Plasticine may help.)

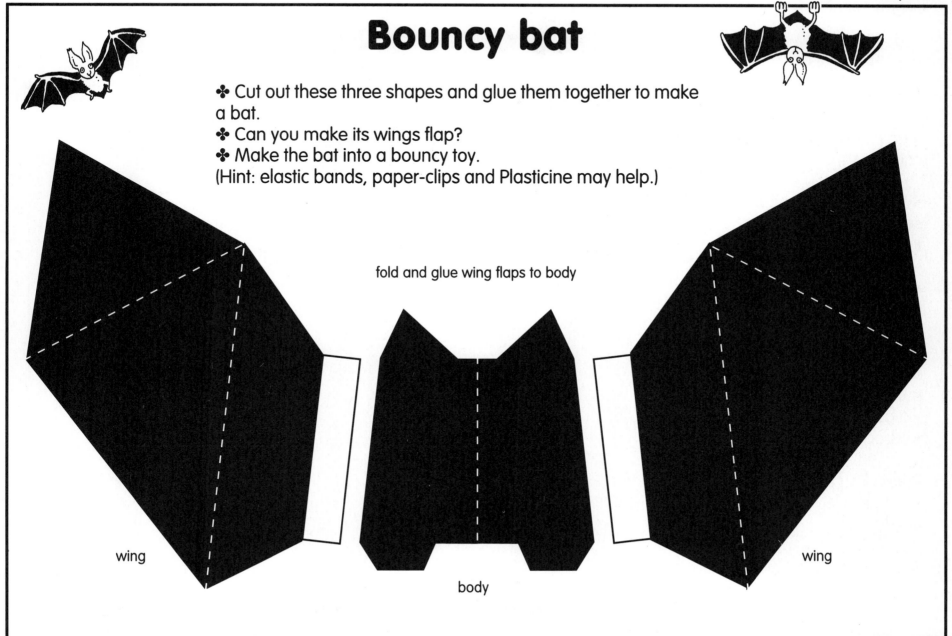

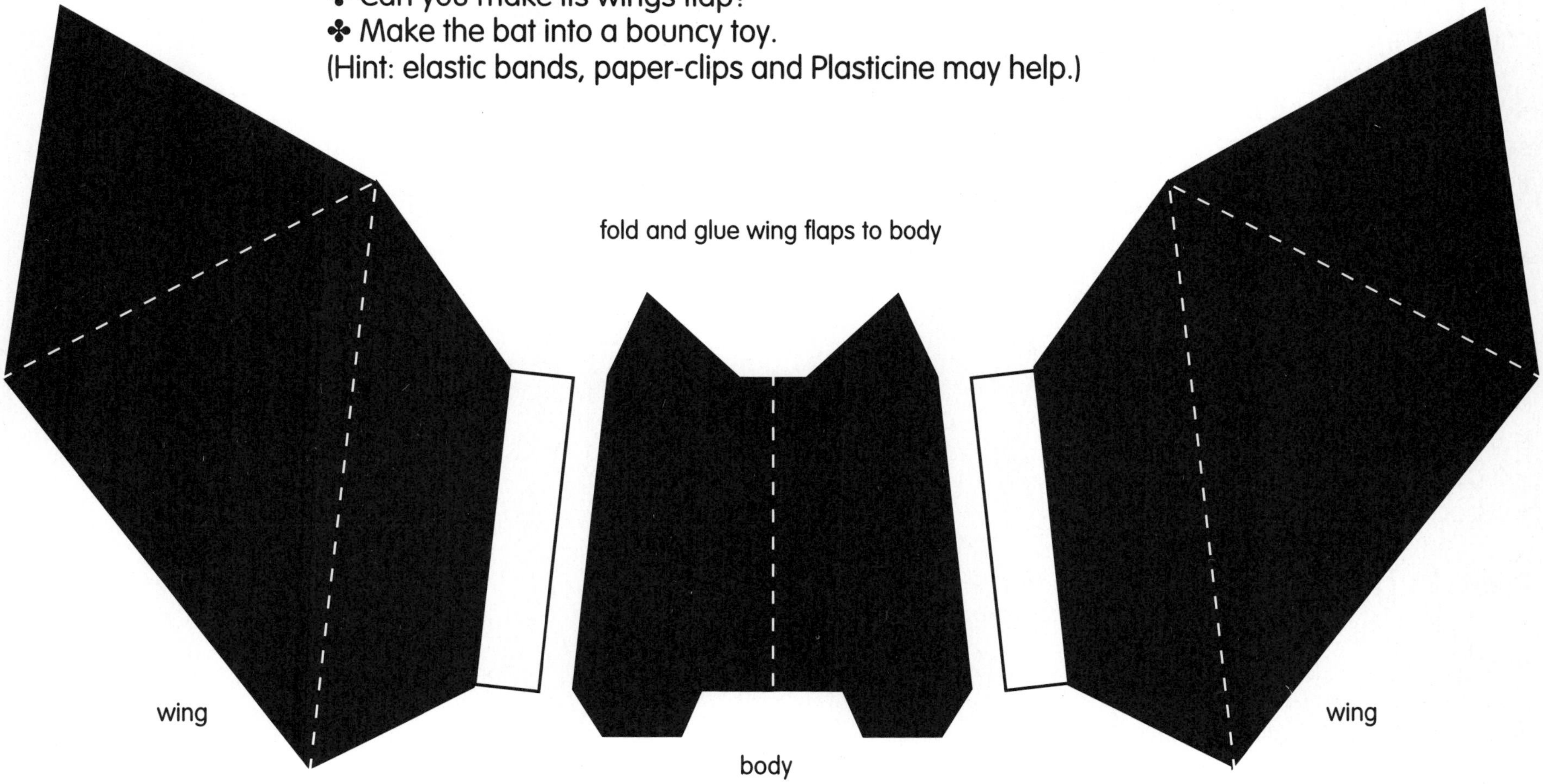

Name ______________________

Make a tangram

Tangrams are ancient Chinese puzzles. A tangram starts from a square. This is then cut into seven pieces. Each piece is called a tan.

✤ Follow these instructions to turn this square into a tangram
- Draw a line from A to B.
- Draw a line from C to D.
- Draw a line from E to F.
- Draw a line from G to F.
- Draw a line from D to H.

✤ Cut the pieces out and use them to make pictures of:

- a person
- a rabbit
- a boat
- a bridge

Rules: You must use all seven pieces for each picture. The pieces must touch but not overlap.

✤ Record your results on a separate piece of paper.

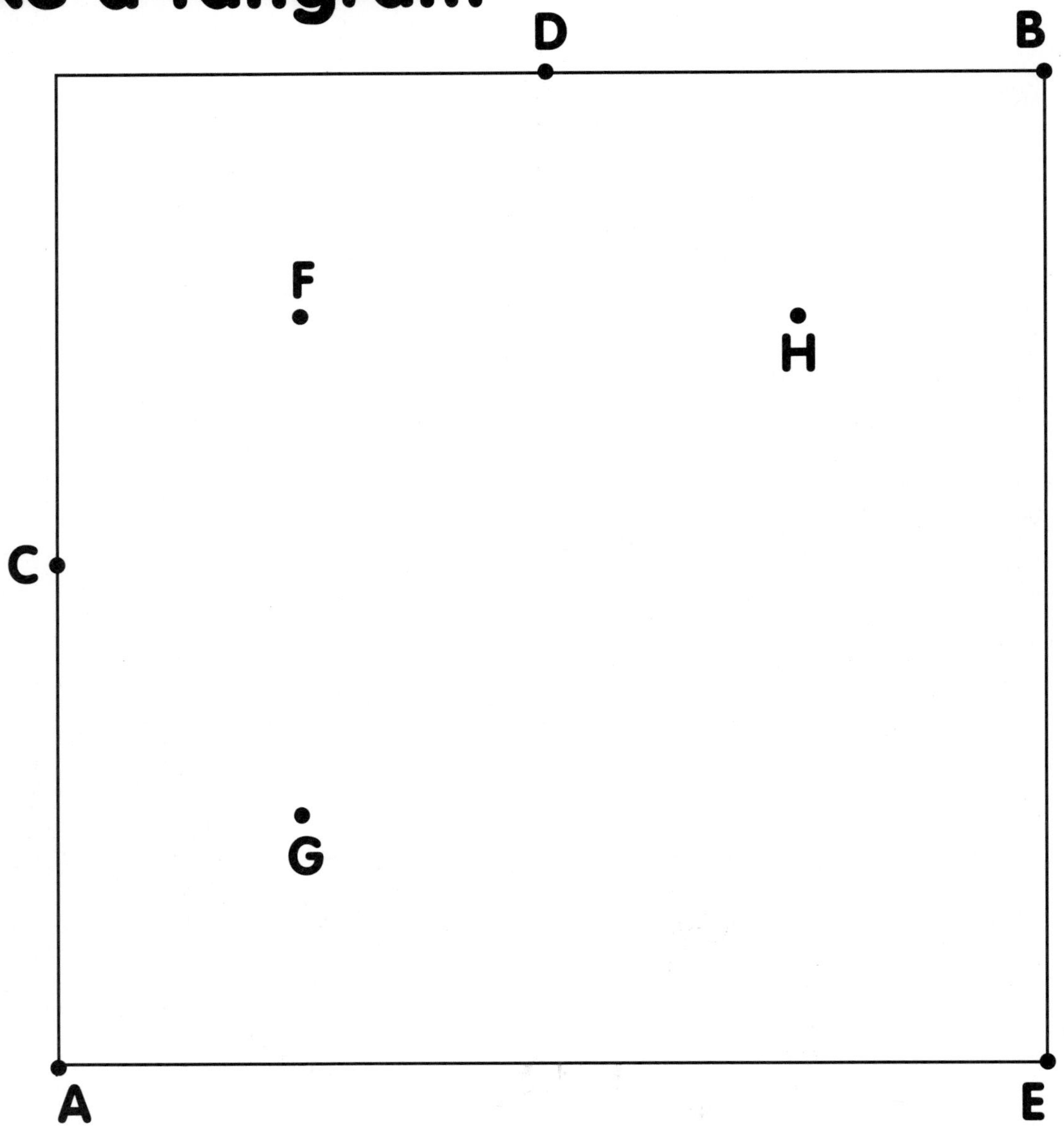

Name ____________________

Play park

✤ Cut out these shapes which show activities in a play park.
✤ Use the grid paper for laying out your design.
✤ Arrange the cut-out shapes in your play park in a safe way. Will any of them need to be left out?
✤ What notices would you display around the park? Where would you put the notices? Draw them on a separate sheet of paper.
✤ Make a model of your play park using a construction kit or scrap materials.

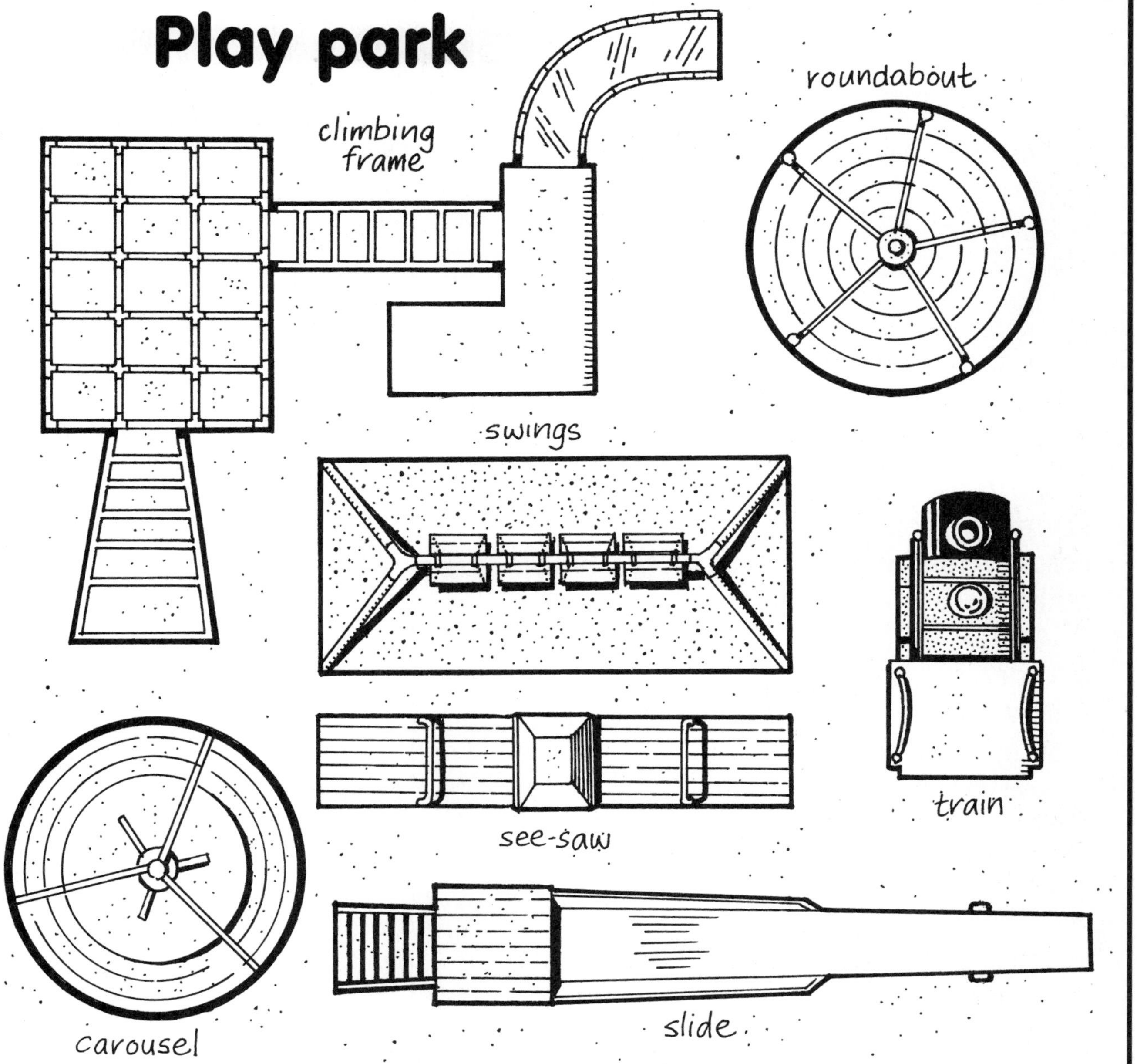

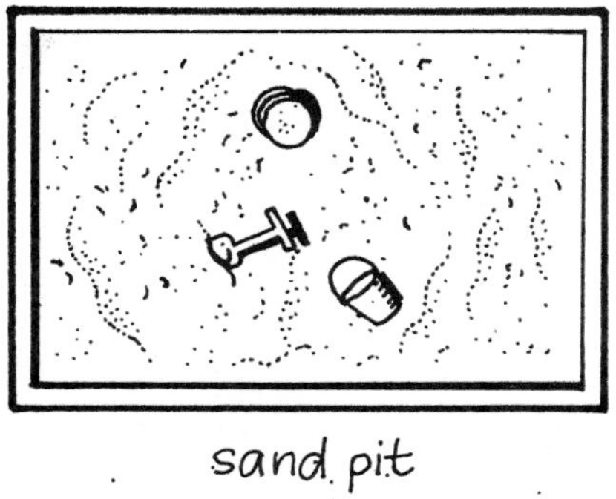

Name ____________________

Board game

Board game

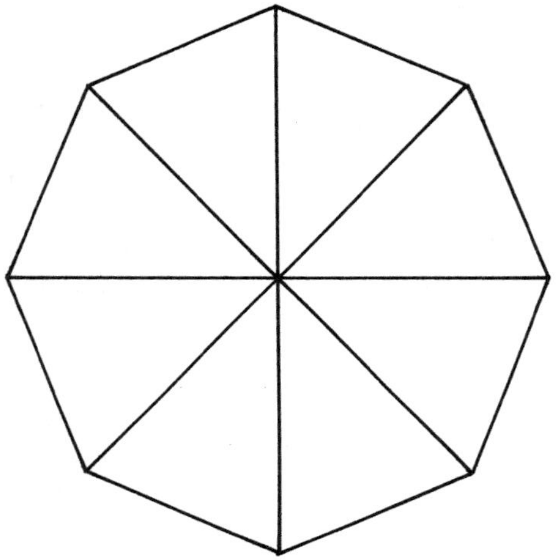

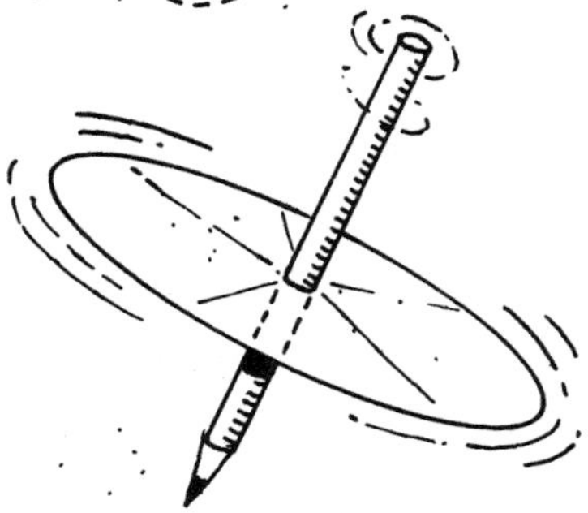

✤ Design and make a board game that uses a die or a spinner or both.
✤ Put the details on the blank die and spinner. Stick them on to card and then cut them out.
✤ Use the planning sheet to develop your ideas.

✤ When you have designed your game, make a prototype from scrap materials. Test your game on children from another class before you make the finished game.

✤ Other things to think about:
- How will you protect your game from tearing or breaking?
- How will you display the rules?
- What sort of container will you keep your game in?

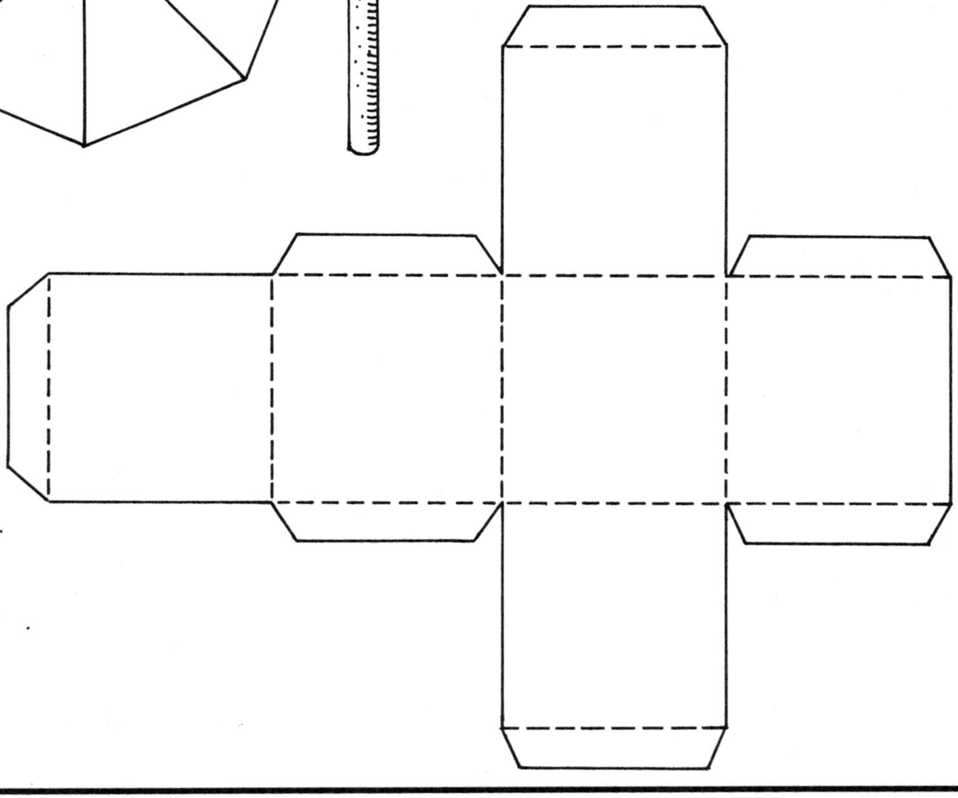

Cinema poster design

Going to the cinema was a popular pastime during World War II. Children had special Saturday morning shows. These usually included cartoons, short films and a serial such as Flash Gordon and Tarzan, or a western such as The Lone Ranger.

✤ Design a poster for children's wartime Saturday morning cinema. Remember to include details such as the date and the starting time.

Name ____________

Party plan

Party plan

A good party needs to be well planned. Below is a jumbled up list of things that you need to do when planning a party.

✤ Cut out the boxes and reorganise them so that the activities are in the correct sequence. You could make them into a flow chart. Add any extra steps that you think are necessary.

- Cook food.
- Decide who is coming.
- Plan games and entertainment.
- Buy food and drink.
- Send out invitations.
- Decide what type of party.
- Decide on the party date.
- Organise prizes for the games.
- Collect replies and work out quantities for food and drink.
- Let the party begin!
- Choose the music.

Design an invitation

✤ Design an attractive party invitation that can be photocopied and then coloured in. Below is a list of information that needs to go on to the invitation. Has anything been left out?

- Whose party is it?
- Why are they having a party?
- Date
- Time
- Place
- Address
- Telephone
- Guests

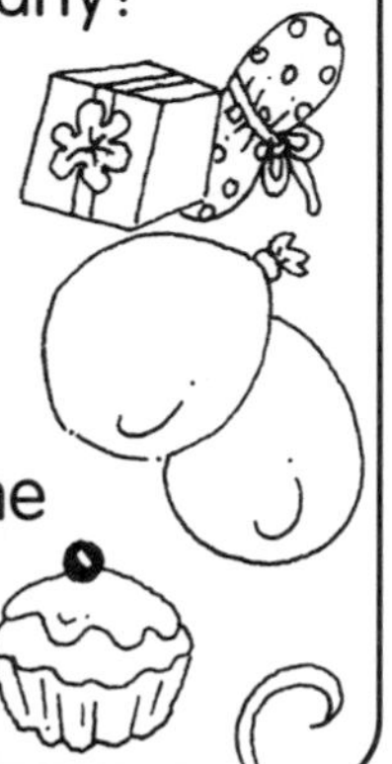

Name ____________

Toys store

Toys store

Do the toys and games in your bedroom end up in a mess?

✤ List below the things that become untidy and need to be stored.

My list

✤ Now make a floor plan of your room.

Mark the doors like this: 

Mark the windows like this: 

Mark the radiators like this: 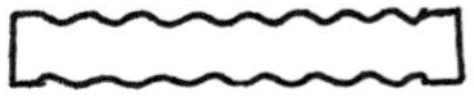

✤ Mark on your plan possible areas that could be used to store toys.

✤ Use the planning sheet to design a toy storage system for your room. Label it to show what each section is for.

✤ Make a model of your toy storage system.

Floor plan

Mobiles

✤ Balance your ruler on your finger as shown below.
How much of the ruler is on each side?

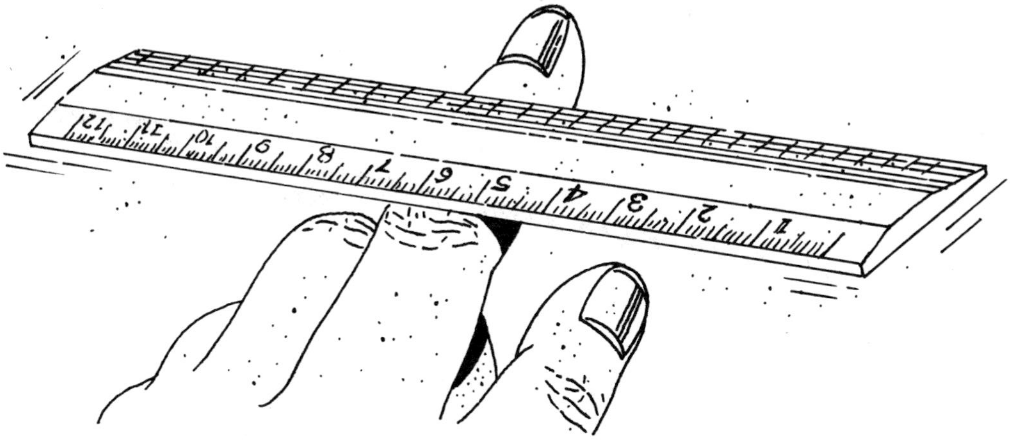

✤ Now tie a piece of cotton around your ruler at the 8cm mark. Does it balance evenly when you hold the cotton?
✤ Add Plasticine to one end of the ruler until it balances horizontally. What do you notice?
✤ Talk to your teacher about your findings.
✤ Now follow the arrangement below to make the piece of dowel balance as well as the ruler.

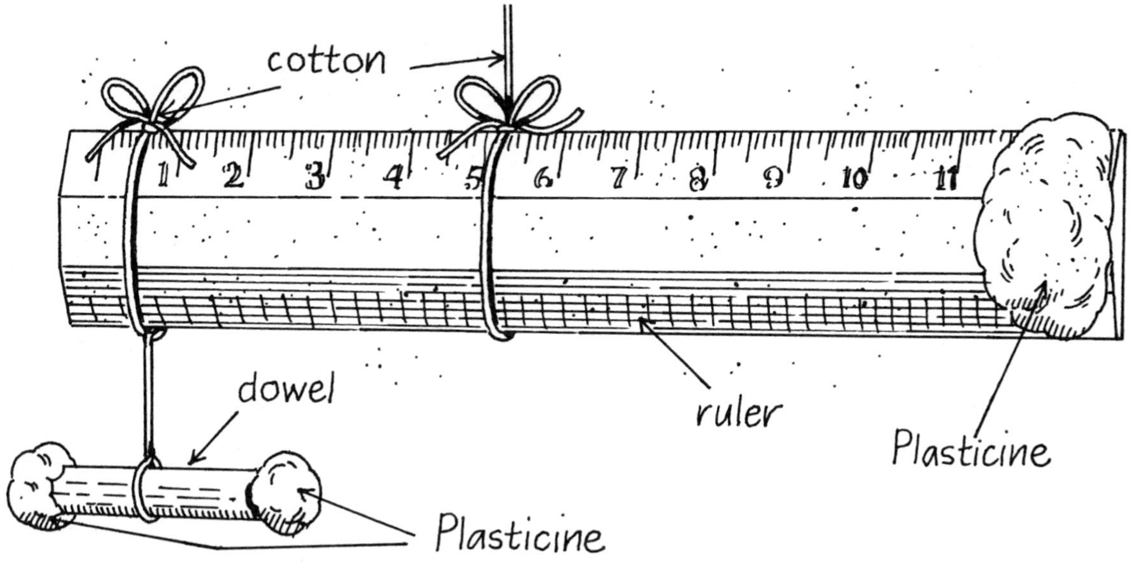

Challenge

✤ Use what you have learned to make a mobile for a young child. You might want to carry out some market research and look at other mobiles. You could ask younger children what should go on the mobile. Do not forget that colour and shape are very important.

Name ____________________

Pitched instruments

Music and dancing were important to both the Ancient Egyptians and the Ancient Greeks.
It was Pythagorus, a Greek mathematician, who discovered the relationship between the length of a piece string and the pitch of a note.

Here are some pitched instruments.

✤ How could you make each one produce a noise?

✤ List other instruments that are played in a similar way.

✤ Use the planning sheet to design your own instrument which will give a range of notes. Make it, if you can.

Name ____________

Sports day

- ✤ You are organising a sports day for your class.
- ✤ List the things you need to think about.
  - What events will you include? Will people need to practise?
  - How will the events be started?
  - How will the competitors know when it is time for their event?
  - Who will record the results?
  - Do you need to provide programmes?

If your plan is a good one, perhaps your teacher will let you hold your own class sports day.

My list

Name ____________________

Wartime play tape

Wartime play tape

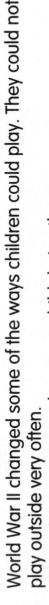

World War II changed some of the ways children could play. They could not play outside very often.

- ✤ Interview someone who was a child during the war.
- ✤ Make a list of questions to ask about his or her play activities.
- ✤ If possible, record your interview on tape.

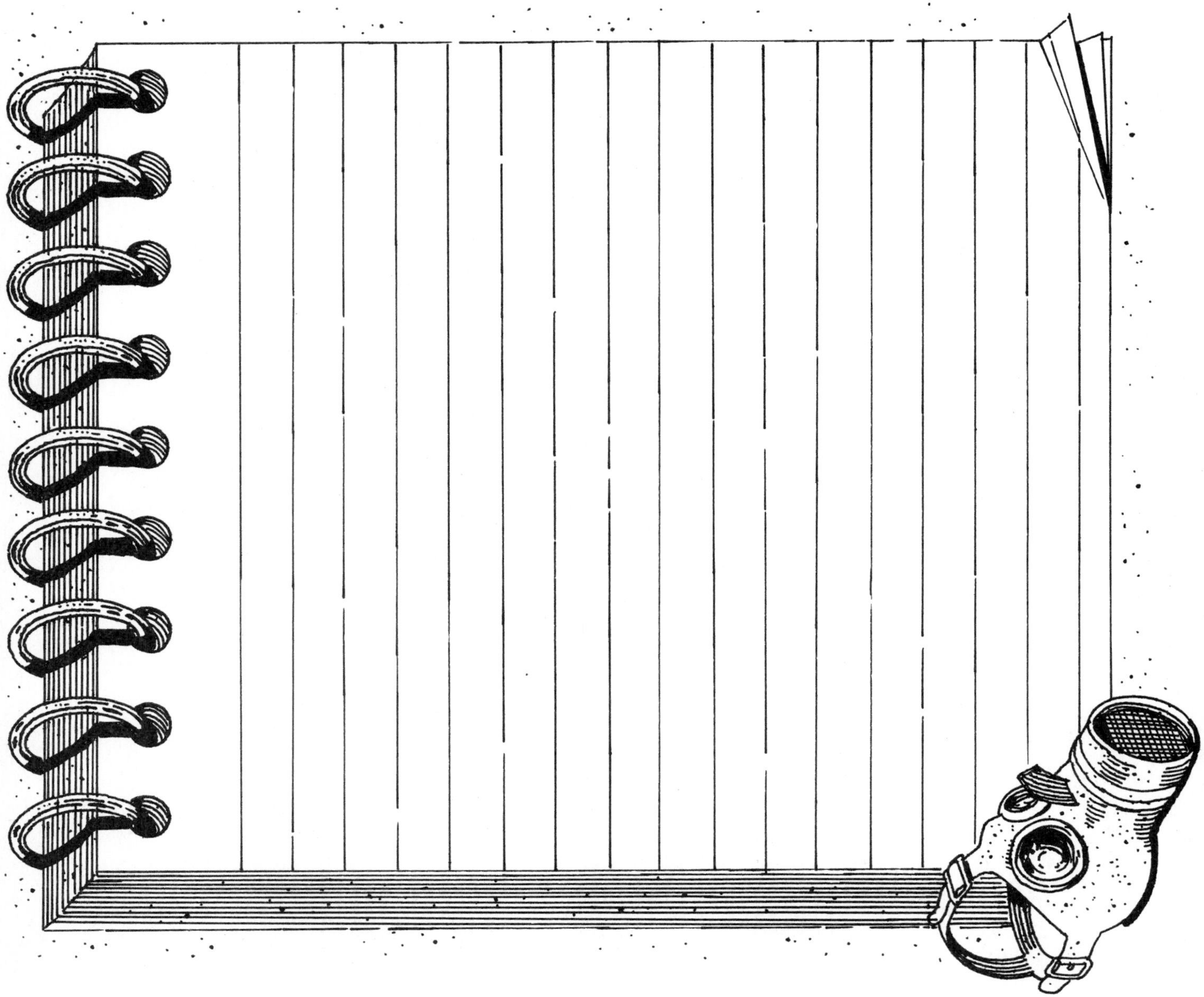

Sound poem

✤ Read this poem.

Pleasant sound

The rustling of leaves under feet in woods and under hedges;
The crumpling of cat-ice and snow down wood-rides, narrow lanes, and every street causeway.
Rustling through wood or rather rushing, while the wind halloos in the oak top like thunder;
The rustle of birds' wings startled from their nests or flying unseen into the bushes;
The whizzing of larger birds overhead in a wood, such as crows, puddocks, buzzards;
And the trample of robins and woodlarks on the brown leaves, and the patter of squirrels on the green moss;
The fall of an acorn on the ground, the pattering of nuts on the hazel branches as they fall from ripeness;
The flirt of the groundlark's wing from the stubbles - how sweet such pictures of dewy mornings, when the dew flashes from its brown feathers!

✤ Think about suitable sounds for each idea in the poem. How could you make each sound? Use the planning sheet to help you.

✤ Make a taped reading of the poem with your sound effects.

Name ____________

Tape slide show

Tape slide show

The diagrams below show how to make a decorative egg.

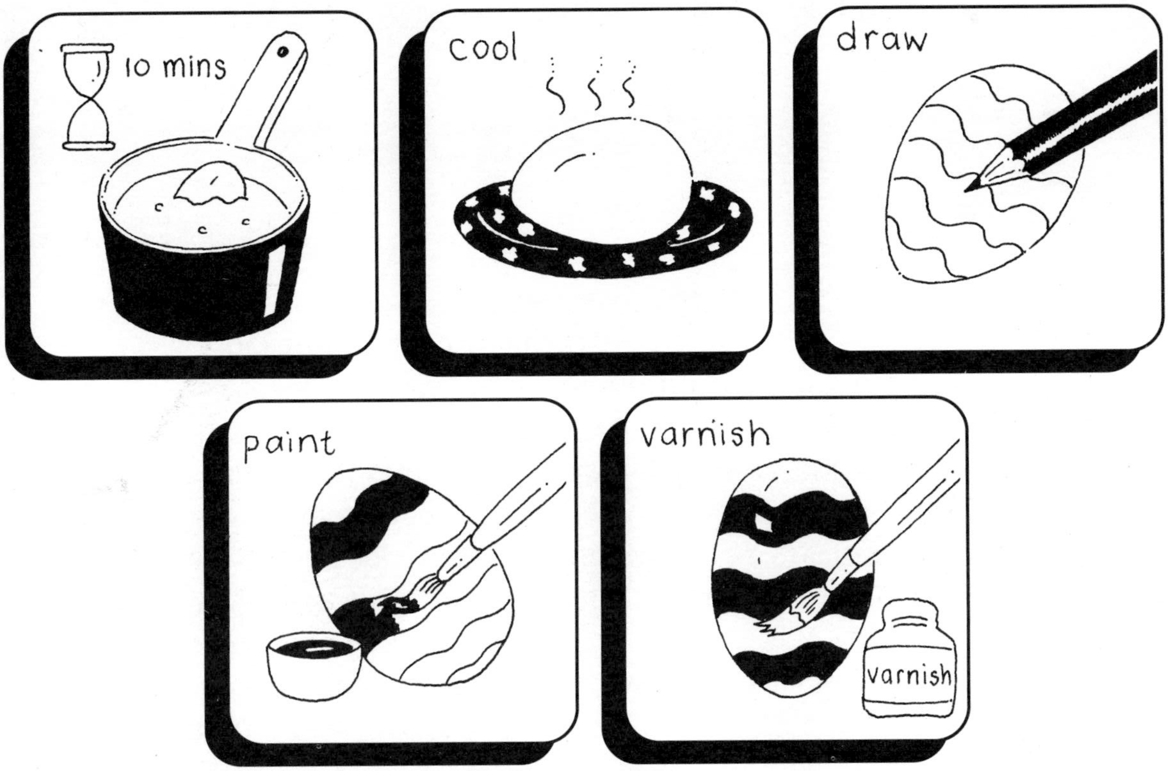

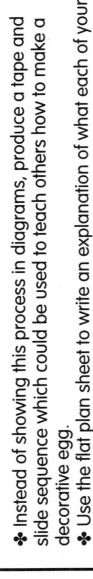

- ✤ Instead of showing this process in diagrams, produce a tape and slide sequence which could be used to teach others how to make a decorative egg.
- ✤ Use the flat plan sheet to write an explanation of what each of your slides will show.
- ✤ Make the egg, taking photgraphs at each stage.
- ✤ For each picture you take, you need to write out the commentary on a separate sheet. Record your reading of this on to tape.
- ✤ When your photographs are ready, project them on to a screen while you play the commentary.
- ✤ How will you know when to change the slide at the end of each section of the commentary?
- ✤ Show the finished product to the class.
- ✤ If you do not have a camera, you could draw the pictures.

Animal homes

✤ In each box, draw a picture of the type of home in which the animal lives. Fill in the words. One has been done for you. Now make up one of your own.

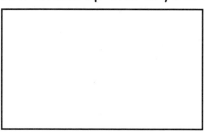

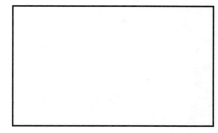

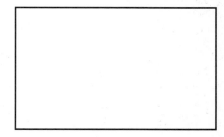

b i r d

n e s t

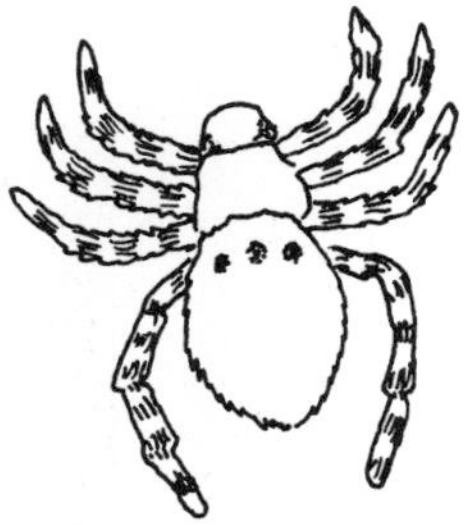

Name ____________________

Animals in the garden

Animals in the garden

✤ List ten animals that you might find in your garden.

Animals

1 ____________________

2 ____________________

3 ____________________

4 ____________________

5 ____________________

6 ____________________

7 ____________________

8 ____________________

9 ____________________

10 ____________________

✤ Choose one of the animals and draw a picture of it below. Label your picture.

✤ Why do you think this animal lives in your garden?

✤ What sort of home does it have?

✤ What does it eat?

✤ Does anything eat this animal?

✤ Is this animal a pest or do you think it is good for the garden?

My picture

Name ____________________

Sitting comfortably?

Chairs are often designed for special purposes.

✤ Cut out the people at the bottom of the page and stick each one underneath the chair on which they might sit.

✤ List other types of chairs. Who uses them?

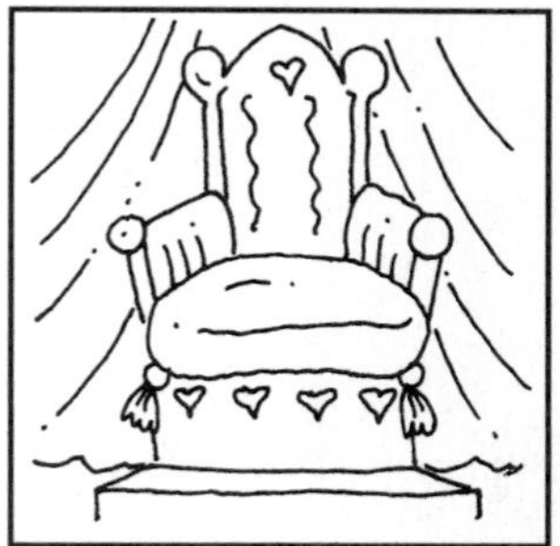

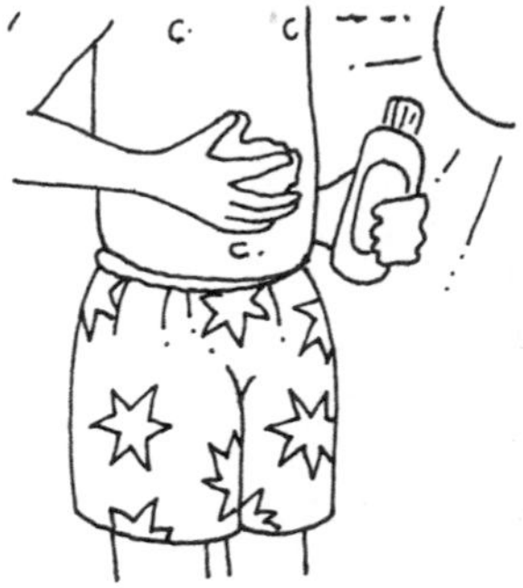

Name ______________________

Framed!

Framed!

Here is an old-fashioned picture frame.

✤ On another piece of paper draw a picture of your face to fit the frame.

✤ Cut out your picture. Stick it into the frame.

(Hint: a mirror might help.)

Word puzzles

Here are ten words to do with houses and homes.

ceiling kitchen door garage roof wall attic garden chimney shed

✤ Can you find them in the puzzle? Look carefully. They may read across or downwards.
✤ Ring each one as you find it. One has been done for you.

✤ Make your own word puzzle in the grid below.

g	d	e	c	e	i	l	i	n	g
a	f	w	f	k	x	w	a	q	l
r	g	a	t	t	i	c	s	m	g
a	c	l	q	s	a	h	d	n	k
g	v	l	p	h	m	i	f	b	i
e	a	h	z	e	n	m	g	v	t
t	g	a	r	d	e	n	t	c	c
y	d	i	o	h	p	e	r	s	h
k	d	o	o	r	h	y	e	s	e
e	l	g	f	w	f	n	w	y	n

Name ______________

Make it bigger

Make it BIGGER

Here is a picture of a house.

✤ Draw the same house twice as big.

✤ Now draw it four times bigger.

(Hint: would squared paper help?)

Name ______________

Standing cactus

Here are two stem shapes of a cactus.
- ✤ Stick them on to thin card and cut them out.
- ✤ Use them to make a standing cactus plant.
- ✤ Add your own prickles, flowers and colours.

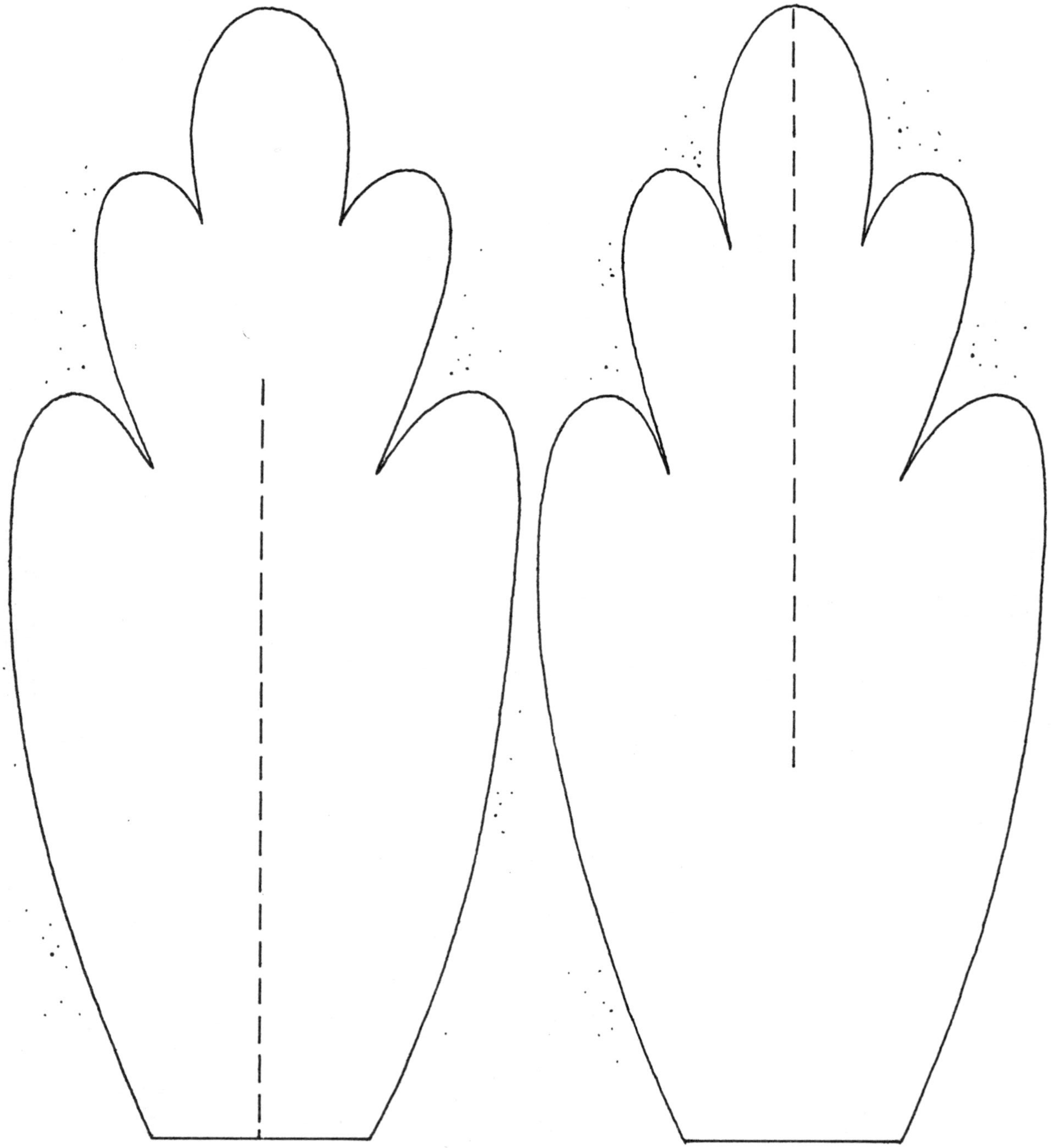

(Hint: cutting along the dotted line may help.)

✤ Now make a pot for your plant.

Name ____________________

Houses in harmony

Houses in harmony

If things work or fit together well, we can say they are in harmony.
Sometimes things are in harmony because they are the same size.

✤ Make the missing houses the same size so that the finished row is in harmony.

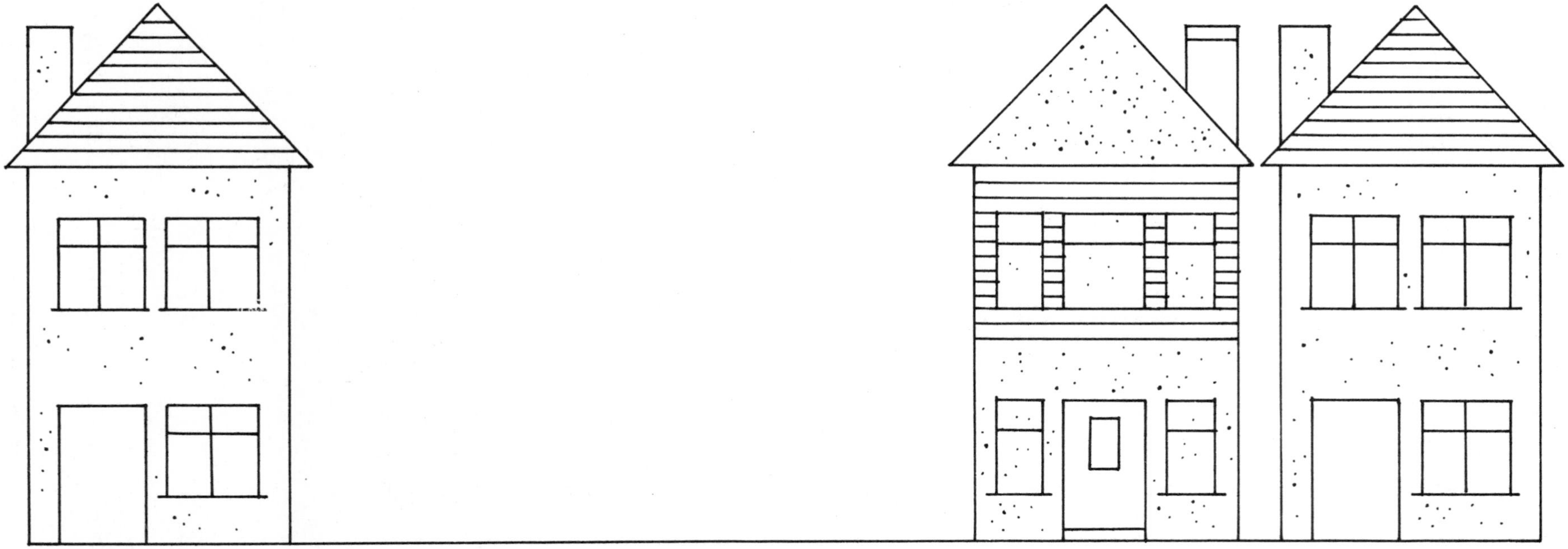

Name ____________________

Ways in

✤ Where do the doors belong in each of the pictures?
✤ Using thin card and sticky tape, make a door to fit each one.

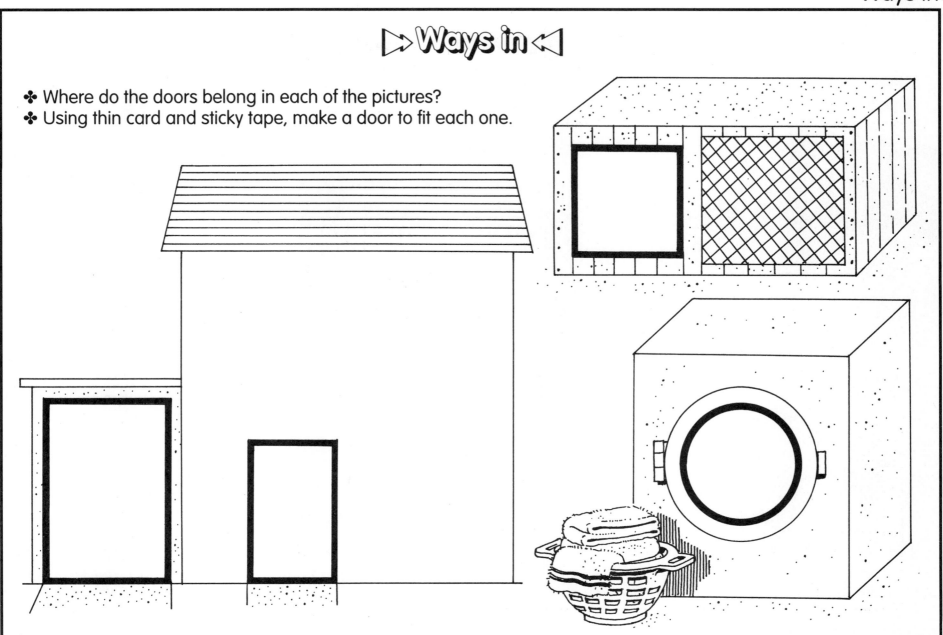

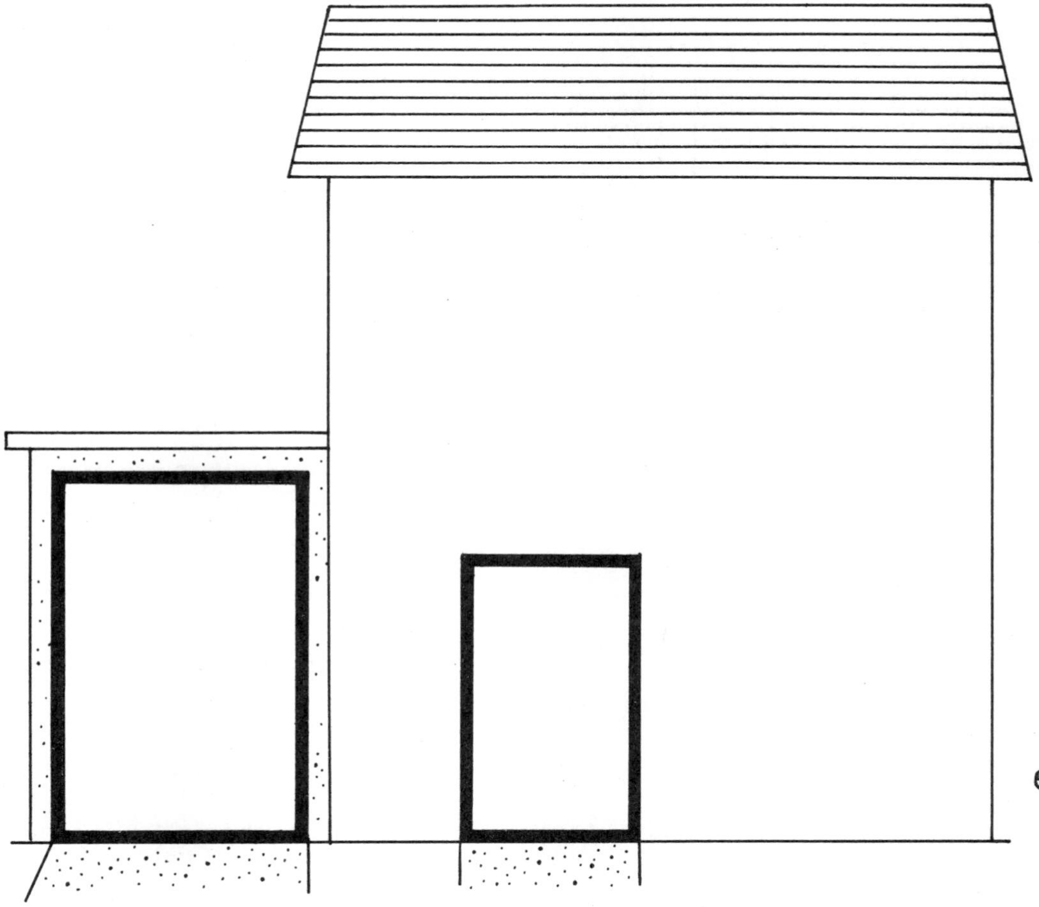

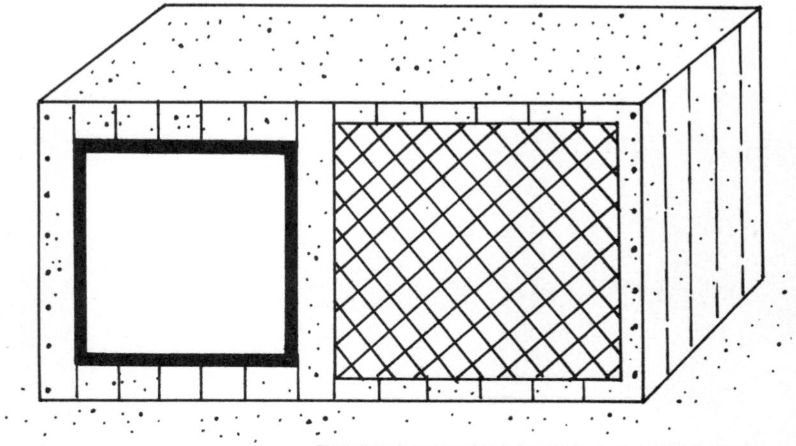

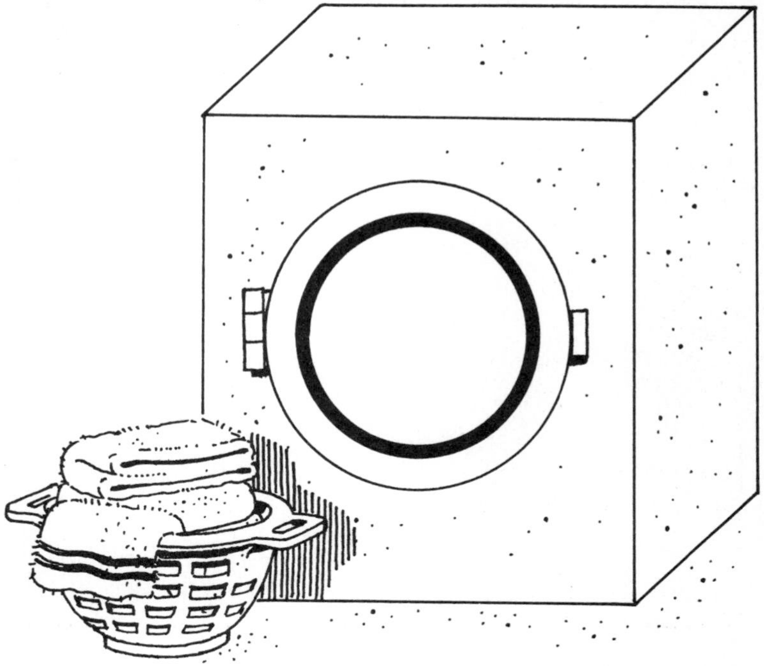

Name ____________________

Garden plants

Garden plants

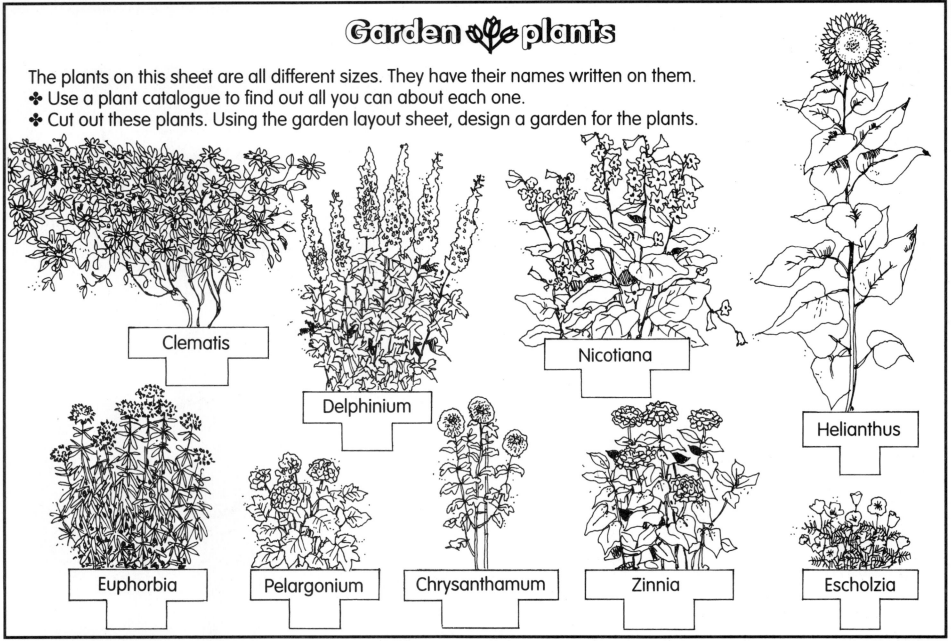

The plants on this sheet are all different sizes. They have their names written on them.

- Use a plant catalogue to find out all you can about each one.
- Cut out these plants. Using the garden layout sheet, design a garden for the plants.

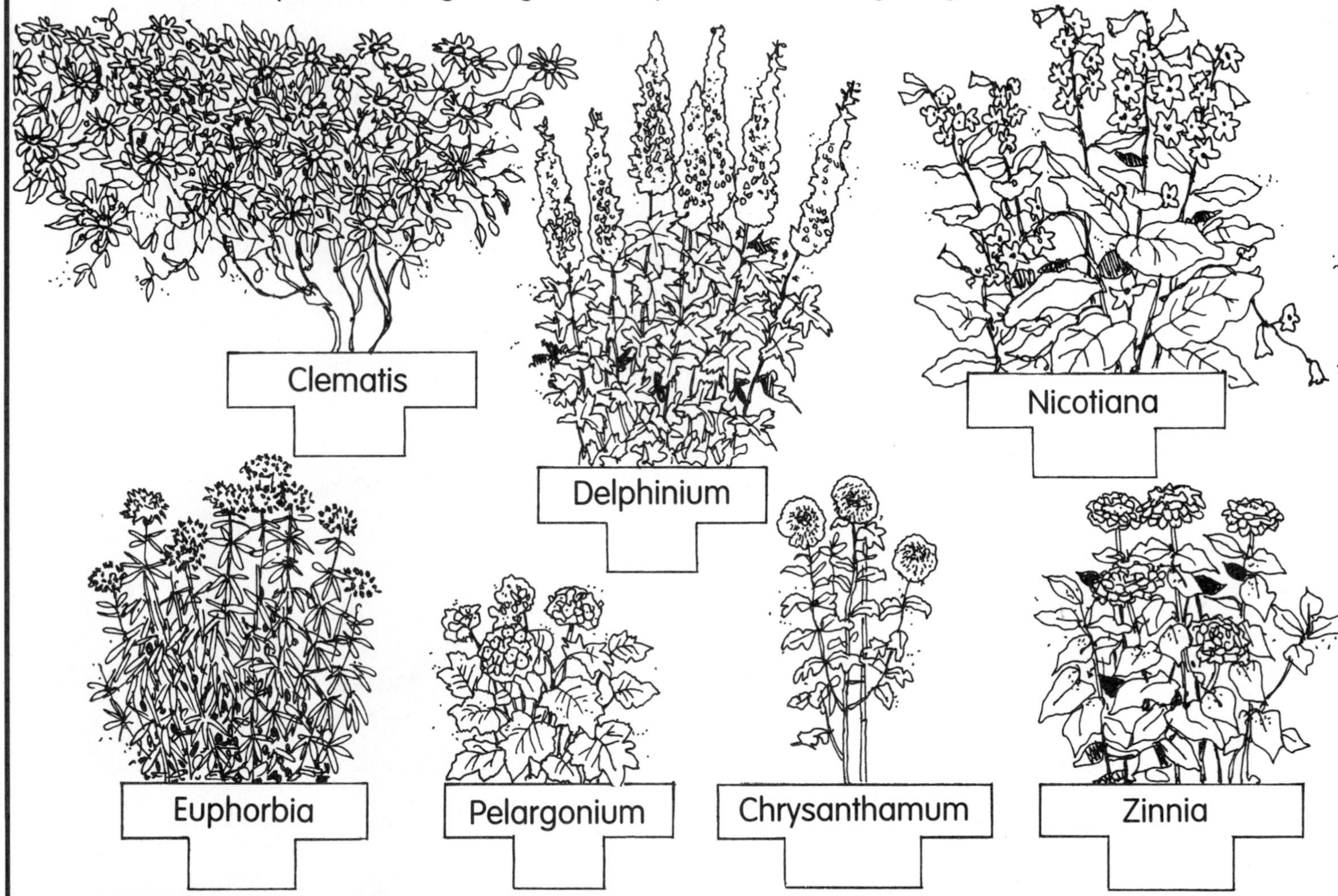

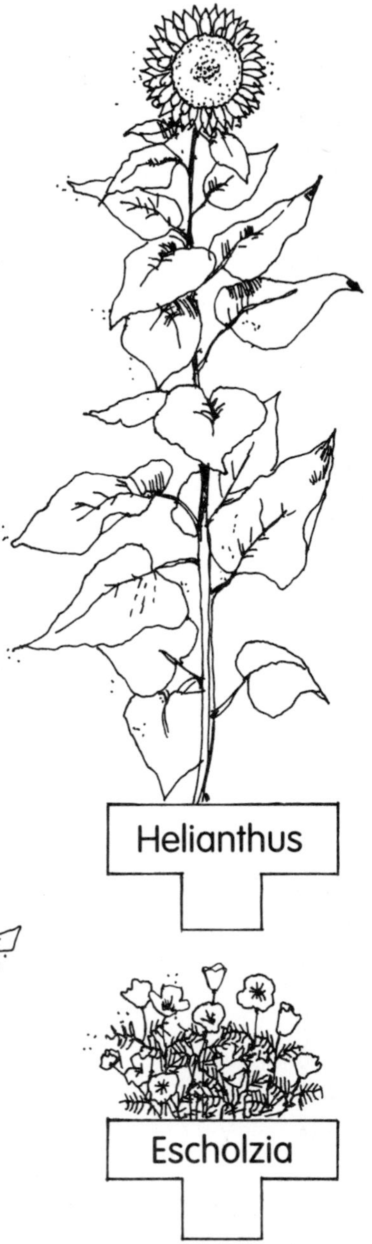

Name ____________________

Garden layout

✤ Design your garden layout on this sheet. Cut slots in the dotted lines below to insert your flowers.

- -

- -

- -

✤ Use the grid paper to draw a plan of your garden.

Name ____________________

Mosaic floors

Mosaic floors

✤ The Romans made floor patterns using coloured tiles. They would lay the tiles in a way that created a picture. These floors were called mosaic floors. The picture shows a mosaic floor made up of lots of small tiles.

✤ Use the grid paper to design your own mosaic picture.
✤ Make your mosaic picture using squares of coloured paper.
You could display it on a black background.
✤ Can you make your picture using clay? Cut squares from clay. When they are dry, paint them.

Name ____________________

Wellies

- Imagine you are going out to do the gardening.
- Cut out these pictures and put them in the correct order.

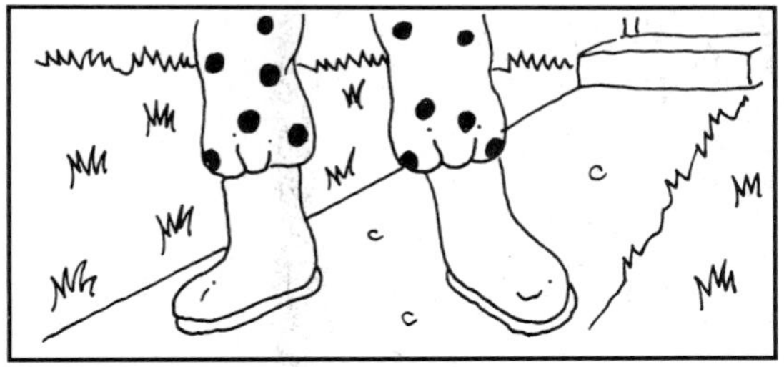
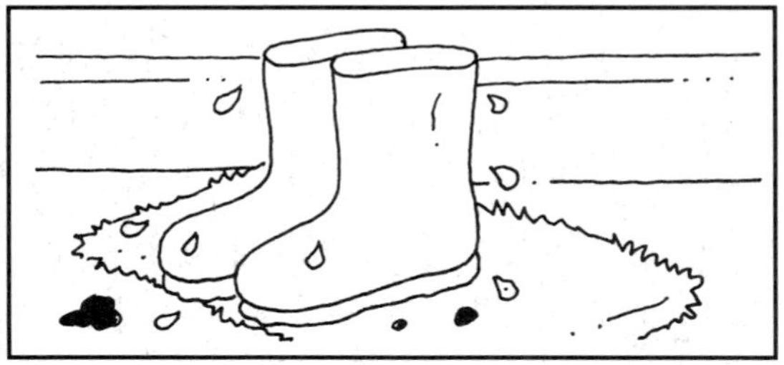
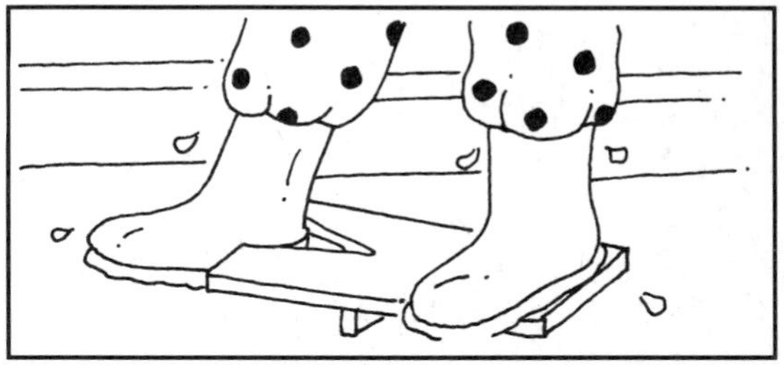
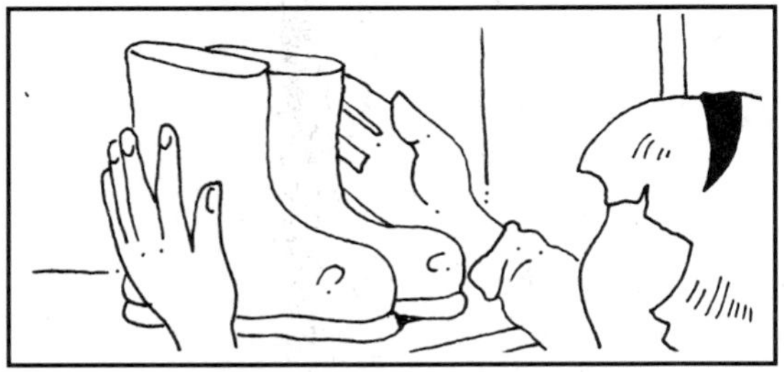
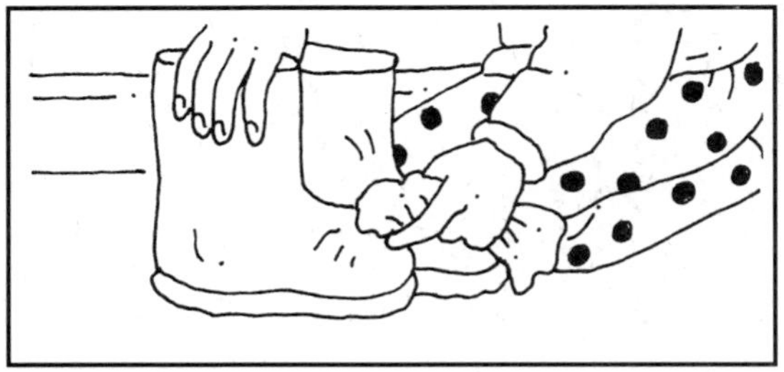
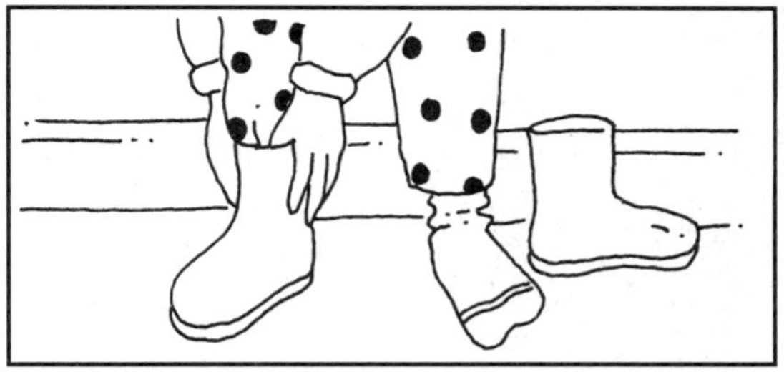

- List reasons for wearing wellies.

1 ____________________
2 ____________________
3 ____________________
4 ____________________
5 ____________________

- List the problems with wearing wellies.

1 ____________________
2 ____________________
3 ____________________
4 ____________________
5 ____________________

- Use the planning sheet to design a tool for cleaning dirty wellies without your hands becoming dirty.
- Make a model of your cleaner.

Name ____________________

Book-ends

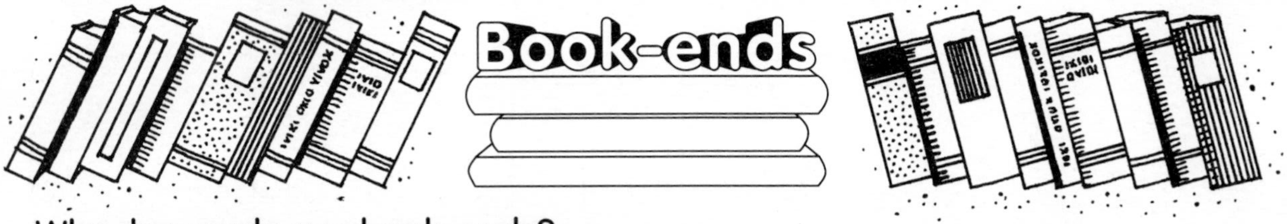

Why do people use book-ends?

✤ Make a collection of different book-ends.

✤ Draw four of them in these spaces.

Which would be best for holding up a large row of picture books?

✤ Design and make a pair of book-ends for a child's paperback collection. They should be colourful and fun. What materials will you use? Use the planning sheet to help you.

✤ How can you stop the book-ends from slipping?

Kitchen tidy

✤ List all the things that might need to be stored in a kitchen tidy.

List

____

____

____

____

____

____

____

____

✤ Look through catalogues for different types of kitchen tidy. Cut them out or draw them in the chart opposite. For each one say what are the best features.

✤ Now use the planning sheet to design your own kitchen tidy. Include the best features of existing models and add special features of your own.

✤ Make a model of your kitchen tidy.

Products already available	Best features

Name ____________________

Planning a bedroom

Planning a bedroom

✤ Using the grid paper and these furniture shapes, design an ideal bedroom.
✤ Cut out the shapes and move them about on the grid. You may want to add other things.
✤ Write down what the dimensions of your room will be and label the furniture. Remember to put in:

windows like this: 

doors like this: 

radiators like this: 

✤ Use a large box to make a model of the bedroom. You could use matchboxes and other scrap materials to make the furniture.
✤ Pretend that you are standing with your back to one of the walls and draw a picture of what you can see in your room.
✤ Use catalogues and paint charts to select how you are going to decorate your room. You should be able to calculate the approximate cost. Do not forget to cost the brushes, turpentine and so on.

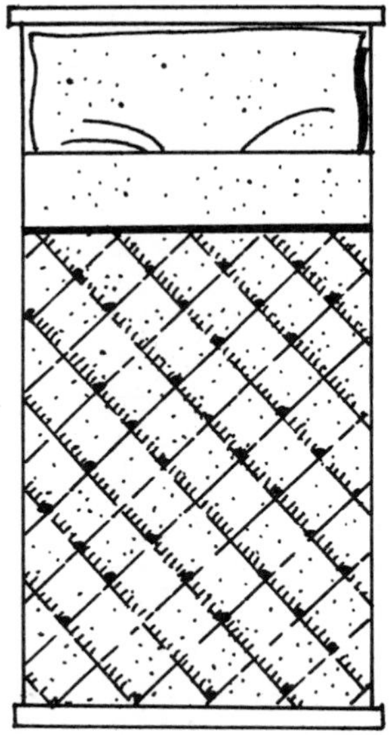
bed

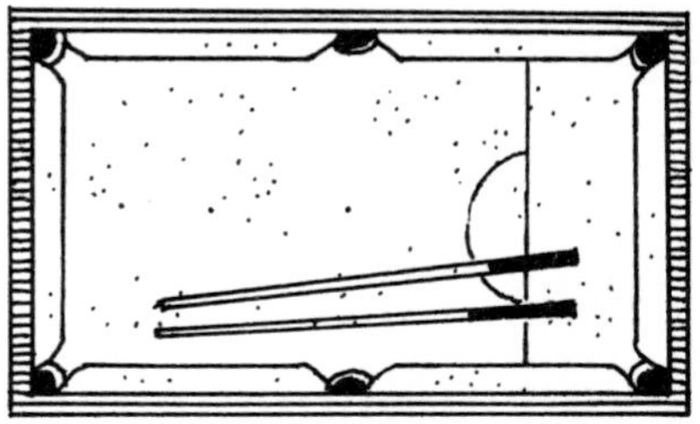
snooker table

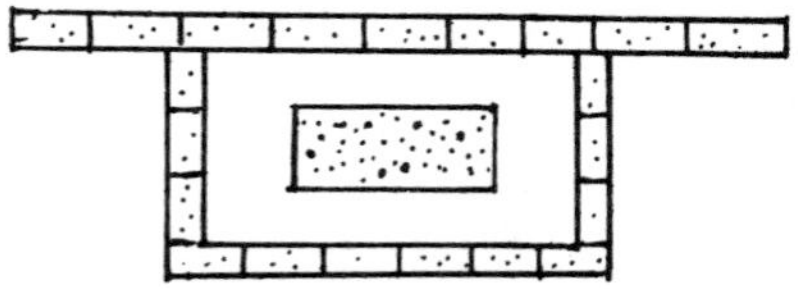
chimney breast

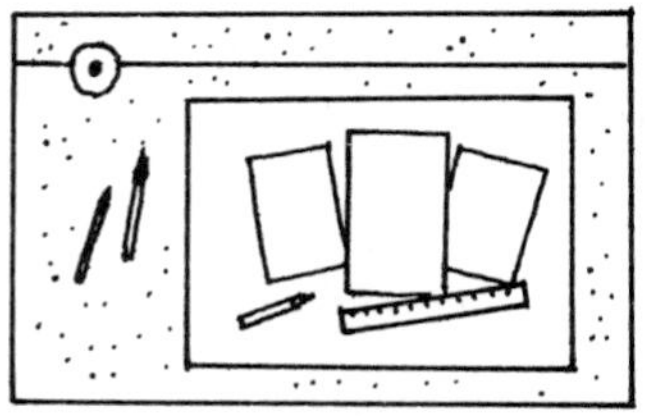
desk

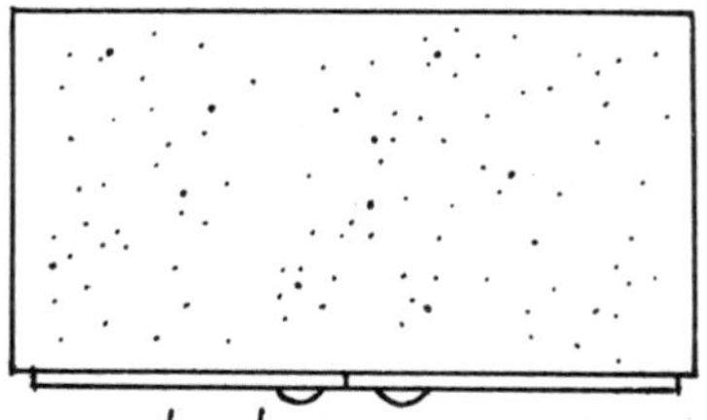
wardrobe

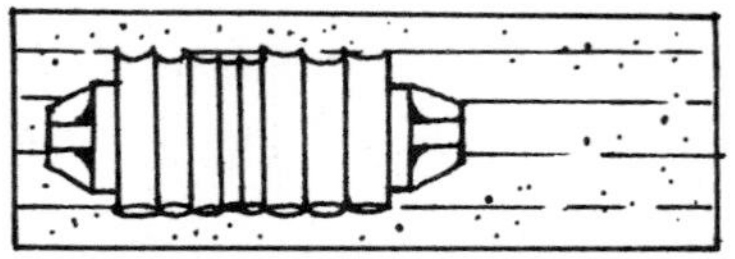
bookshelf

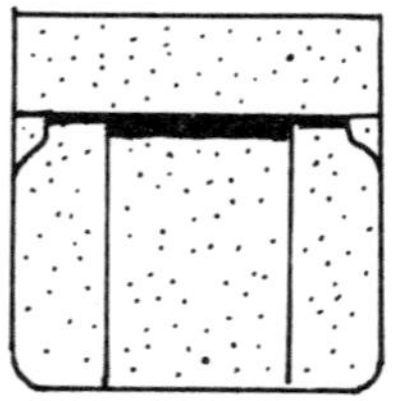
armchair

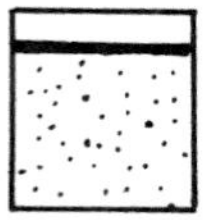
chair

Name ____________

Moving house

You are trying to sell your house.

✤ Make a list of all the good and bad points about it.

Good	Bad

✤ Using the good points, write an advertisement for the newspaper to sell your house.

For sale

____ **bedroomed house in** ____________

Telephone No ________ **Time of visit** ________

It costs 15p per word to place an advertisement in the newspaper.

✤ How much will your advertisement cost?

✤ Using the planning sheet, design an advertising board to put outside your house.

- What information will you put on it?
- What will it be made from?
- How will you fix it outside your house?

Planning a house

Name ______________

Planning a house

This is an elevation view.

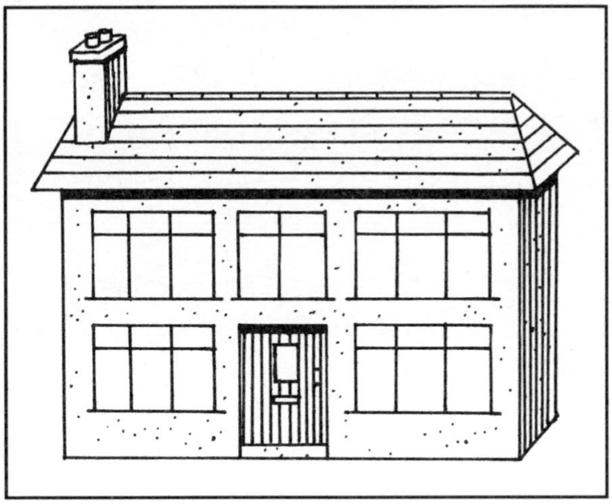

This is a plan view.

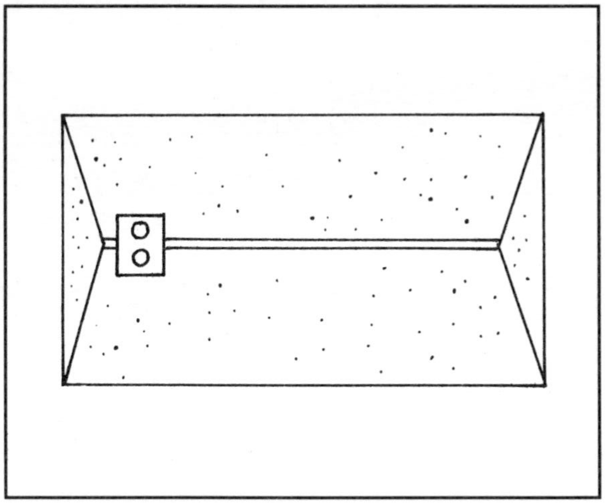

This is a section.

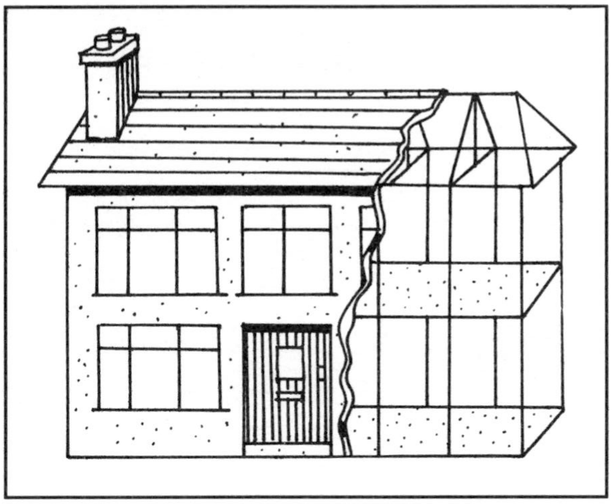

This is an oblique view.

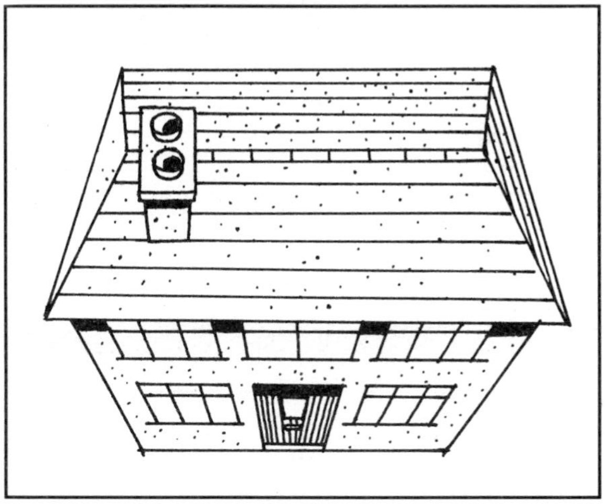

Architects draw all of these pictures of a house so that people can see what it looks like and so that the builders know what to do.

✤ Use the grid paper to design the ground floor of a house you would like to live in.

✤ Label the rooms.

Mark the doors like this: 

Mark the windows like this: 

✤ Now draw an elevation and a section of your house on a separate sheet.

Name ____________________

Roman villa

Here is a layout plan of a typical villa built by the Romans in Britain. It is drawn to scale. The scale is 1cm = 1m.

✤ Work out how big the actual villa would be using this scale.

✤ Using reference books, find some pictures of Roman villas. List the rooms you would want in a villa that you were building. Research, then list, the materials that would be used.

✤ Using the planning sheet, draw a plan of your villa. Draw an elevation view. You might wish to use the same scale as the one for the plan opposite.

✤ Build a model of your villa using materials available in the classroom.

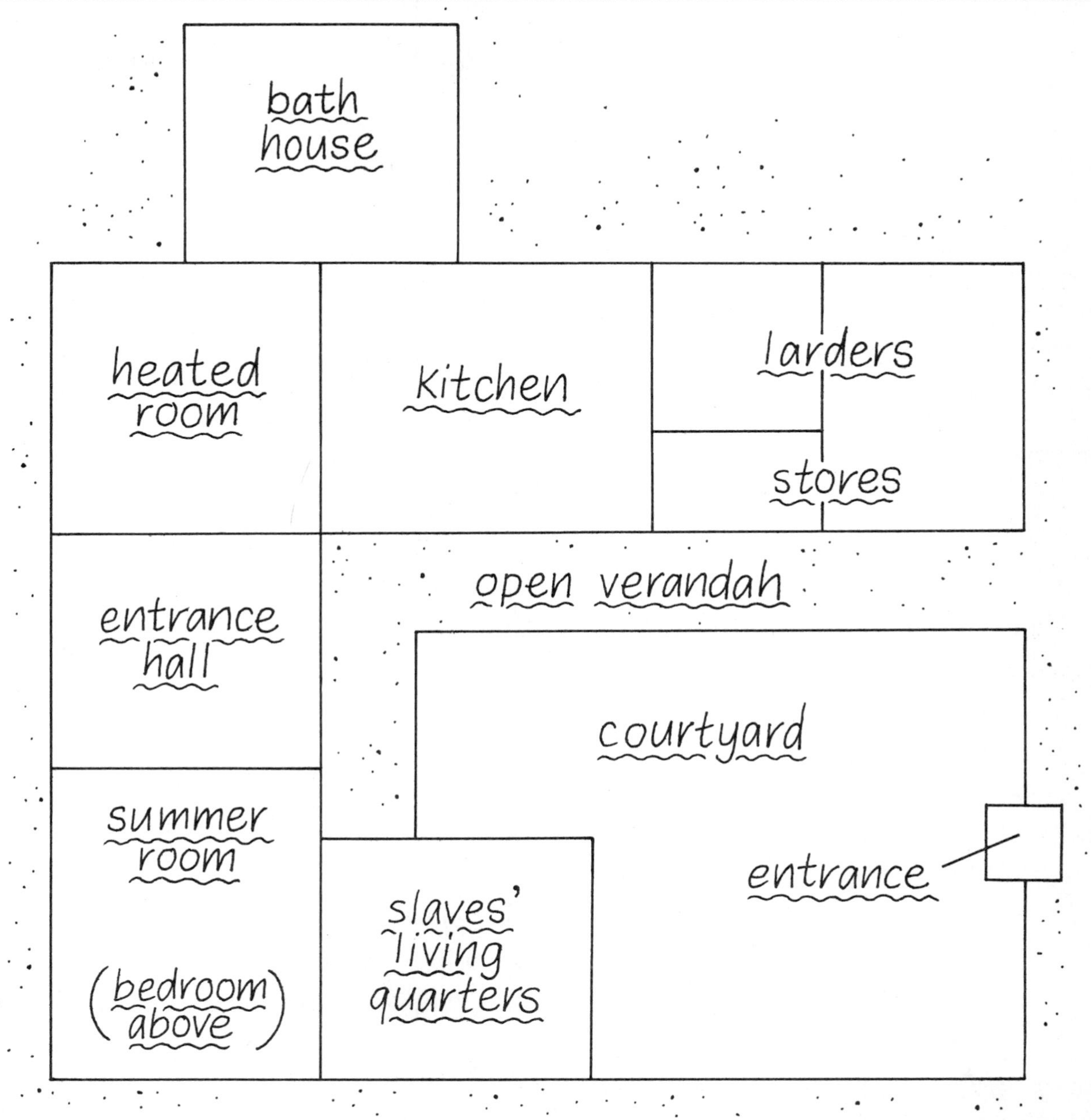

Name ____________________

Burglar proof

Many homes are broken into. House owners try to find ways of stopping this from happening to their home.

✤ Use the grid paper to make a floor plan of your house and mark on it all the ways you could get in.
✤ At each entry point say how you would stop intruders breaking in.
✤ List below some of the other precautions you might take to make your home safe.

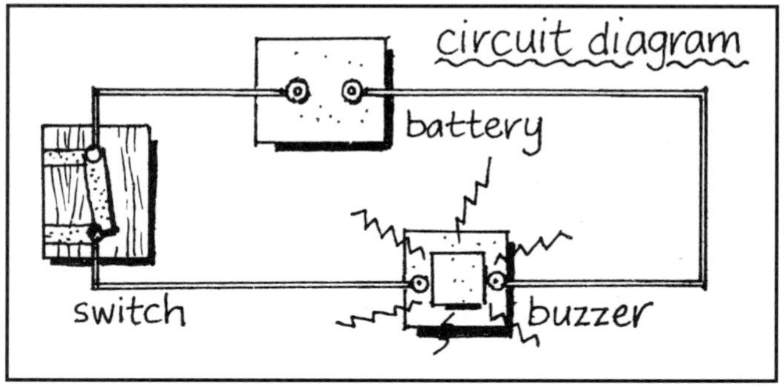

Make a burglar alarm
Burglar alarms are often used on doors and windows.

The three switches drawn here may help you to make a burglar alarm. The electric circuit may help you with the layout. You could make a door from cardboard or wood and the switches from foil. Remember, you do not want the burglars to be able to see the switch from outside.

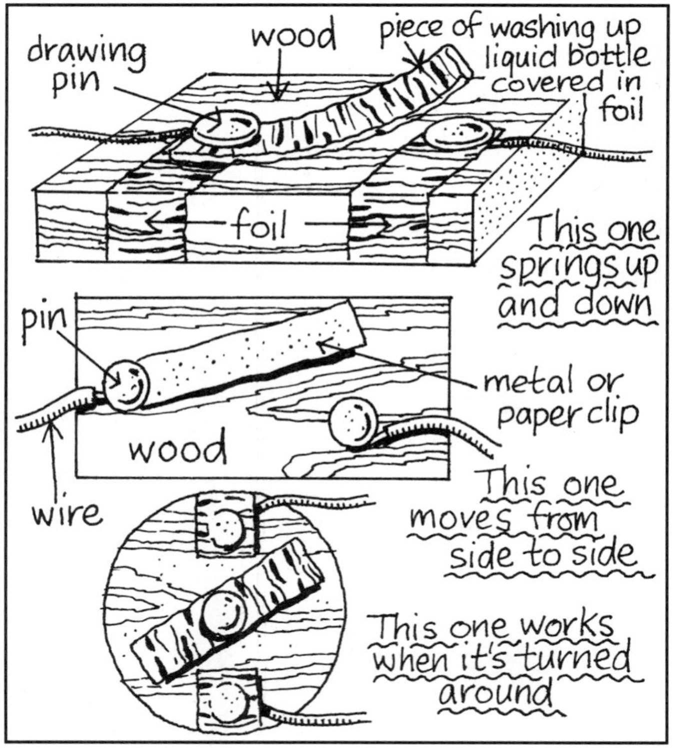

Name ____________________

Design a chair

Many of the chairs we sit in are not the right size for us.

✤ Use the planning sheet to make a chair that will fit you perfectly.

✤ You may want to make a scaled-down cardboard model of yourself to help with your design. You can do this by using split pins and card. Ask a friend to measure you carefully. Make a note of:

Back length ____________________
Hip to knee length ____________________
Knee to ankle length ____________________

✤ When you have built the model figure, make your chair to fit it.

- What materials will you use?
- How will you make your chair strong?
- How will you make it comfortable?
- Which glue will you use?

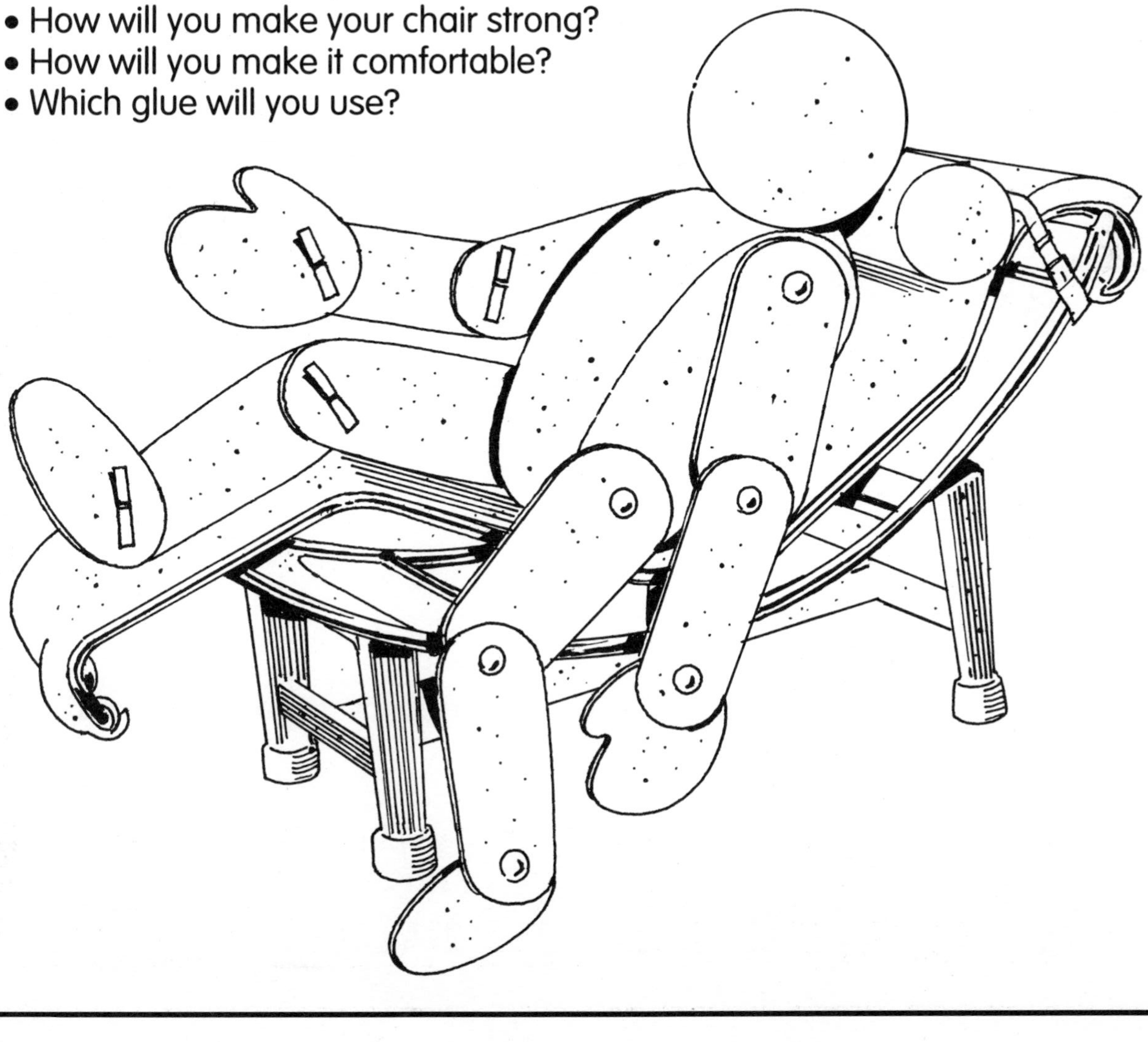

Name ____________________

Think of an apple

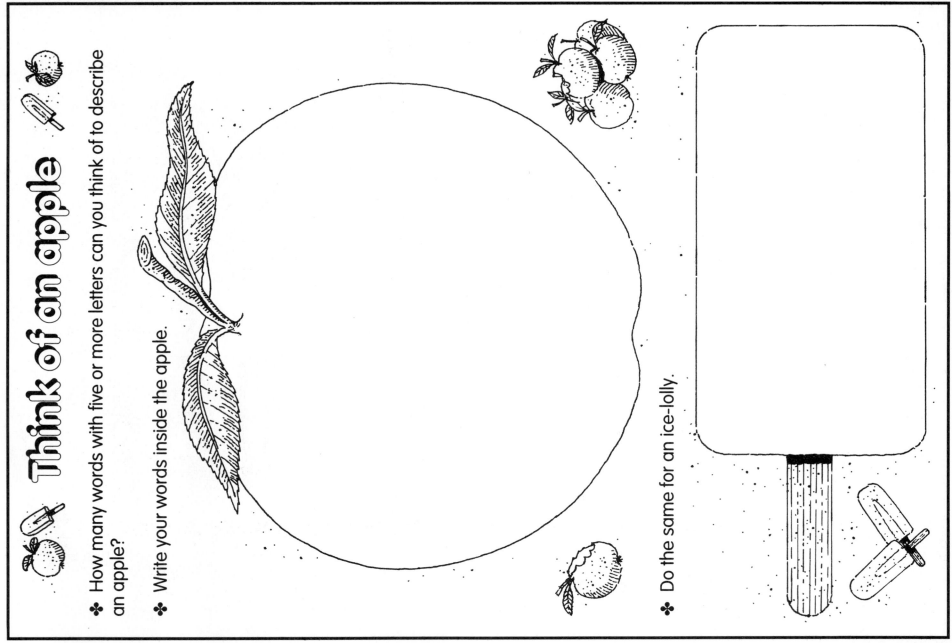

Think of an apple

❖ How many words with five or more letters can you think of to describe an apple?

❖ Write your words inside the apple.

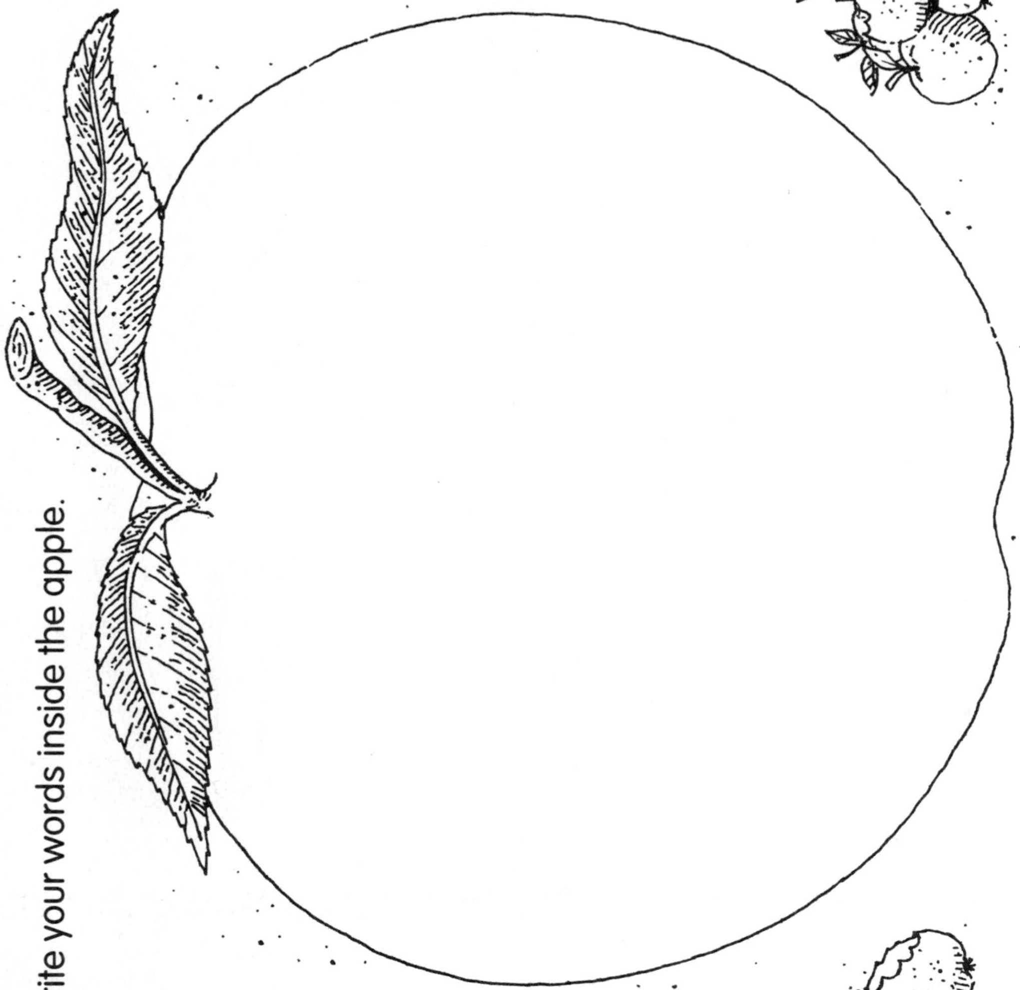

❖ Do the same for an ice-lolly.

Name ____________________

Good taste

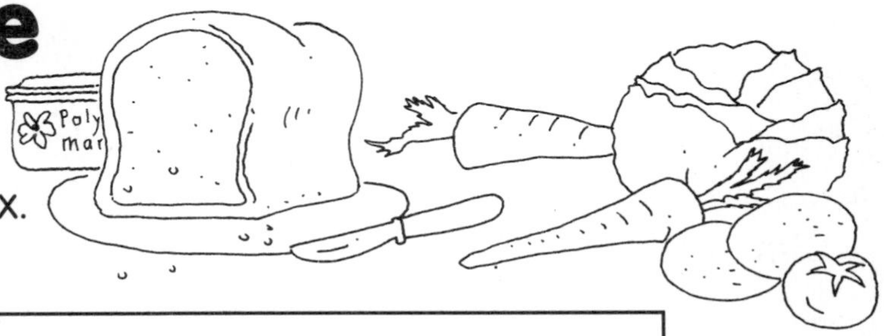

- ✤ List your five favourite foods.
- ✤ Say what each one tastes like. Write at least one word in each box.

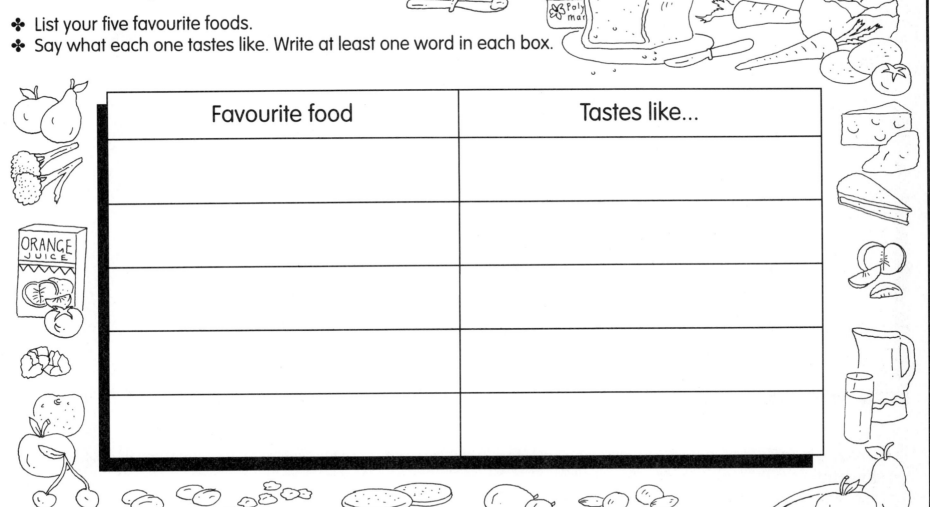

Favourite food	Tastes like...

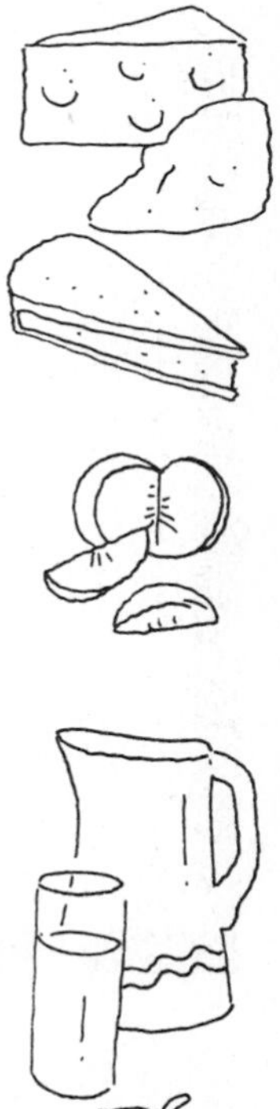

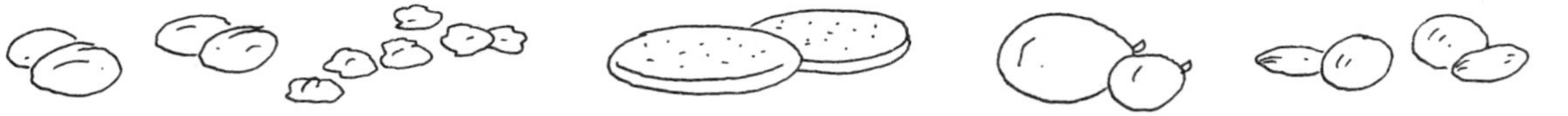

- ✤ Using scrap materials, make a collage picture of each of your favourite foods.

Name ____________________

Tasty tea

Tasty tea

You are going to have tea at a cafe. What will you choose to eat?

✤ Write your ideas here:

My teatime menu

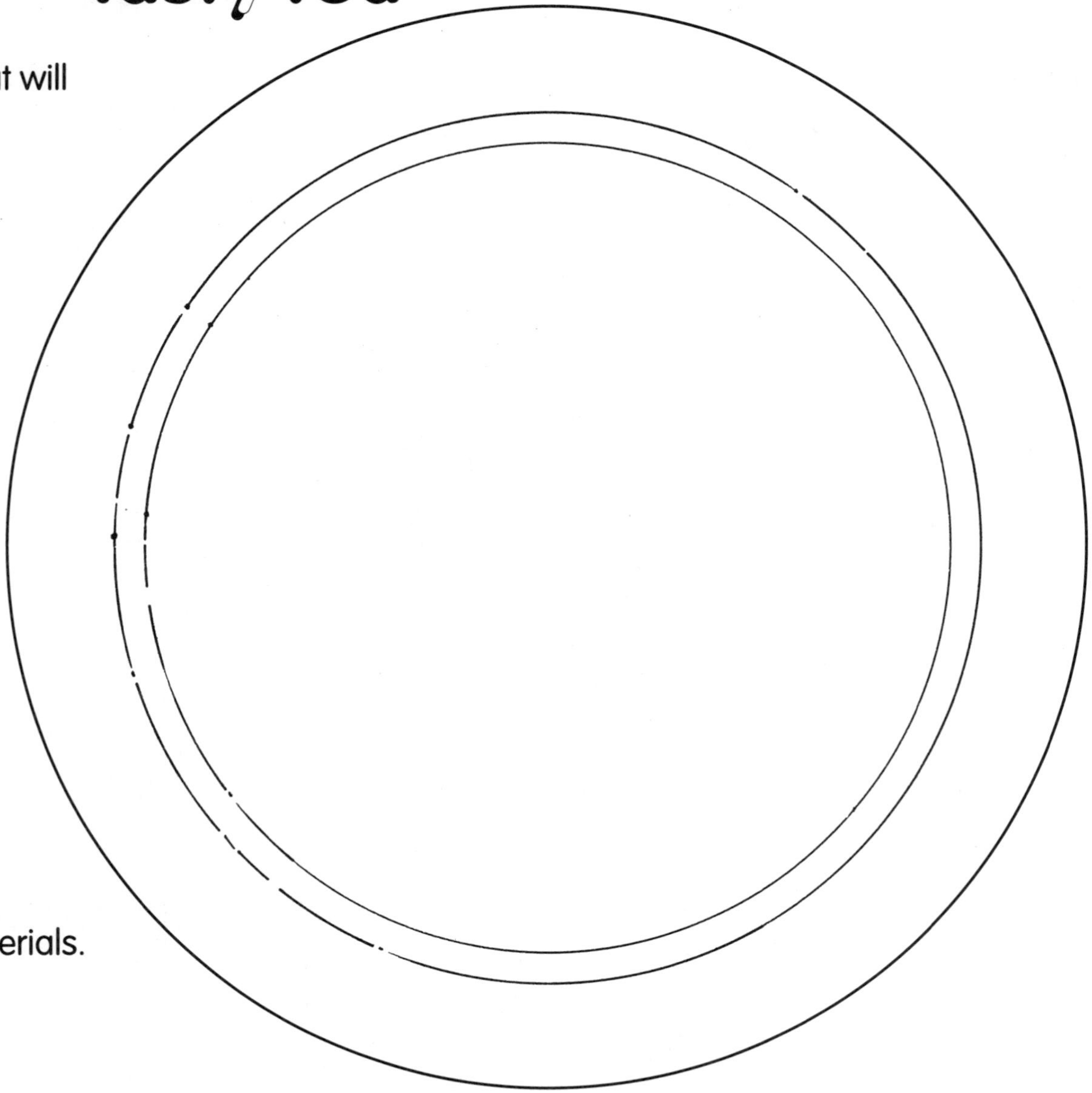

On the right is your empty plate.

✤ Design a border for it.

✤ Now make your meal from scrap materials. It must fit the plate.

✤ Cut out the plate.

✤ Make a place mat for your plate.

Kitchen dangers

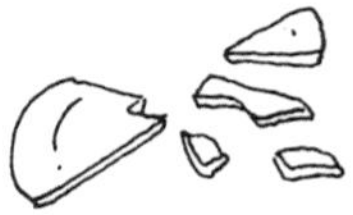

- What are the possible dangers in each picture?
- Write at least one danger in the box next to each picture.
- Write a slogan for each picture that warns of the possible danger.

Danger!

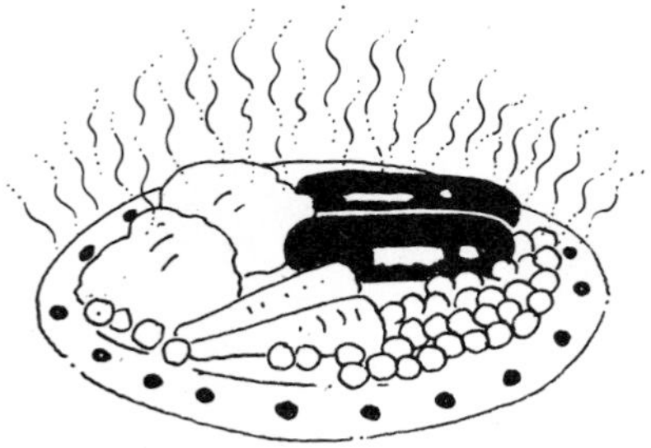

Danger!

Danger!

Danger!

Name ____________________

Talk about teeth

Talk about teeth

Here are some foods.
- ✤ Which ones will harm your teeth?
- ✤ Which ones are not bad for teeth?

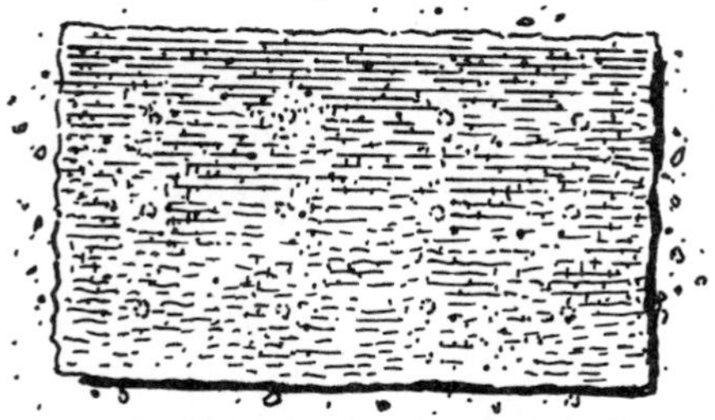

wholemeal crispbread

crisps

apple

tomato

diet cola

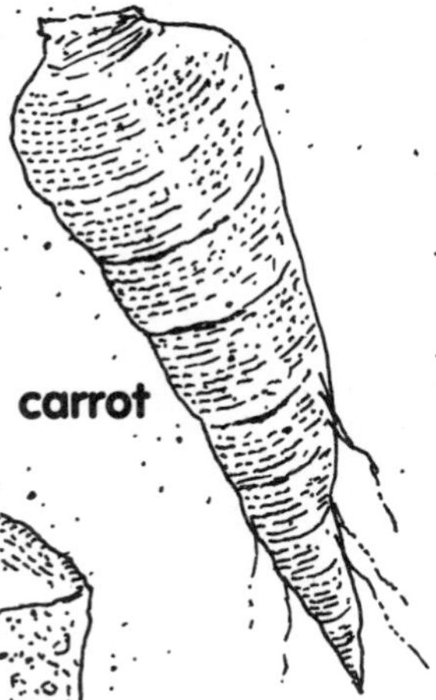

carrot

jam

water

buttered toast

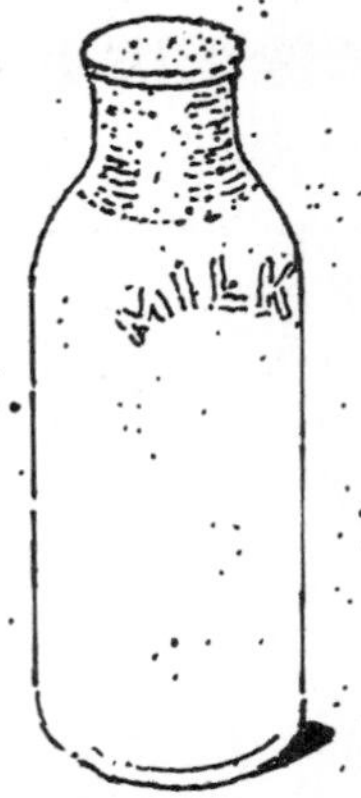

milk

jam sponge

toffee

ice cream

- ✤ Cut out each food and stick it on to one of the teeth on the teeth outlines sheet.
- ✤ Talk with your teacher about why you have sorted them in this way.

Name ____________________

Teeth outlines

✤ Put some healthy foods on this tooth outline.

✤ Put some unhealthy foods on this tooth outline.

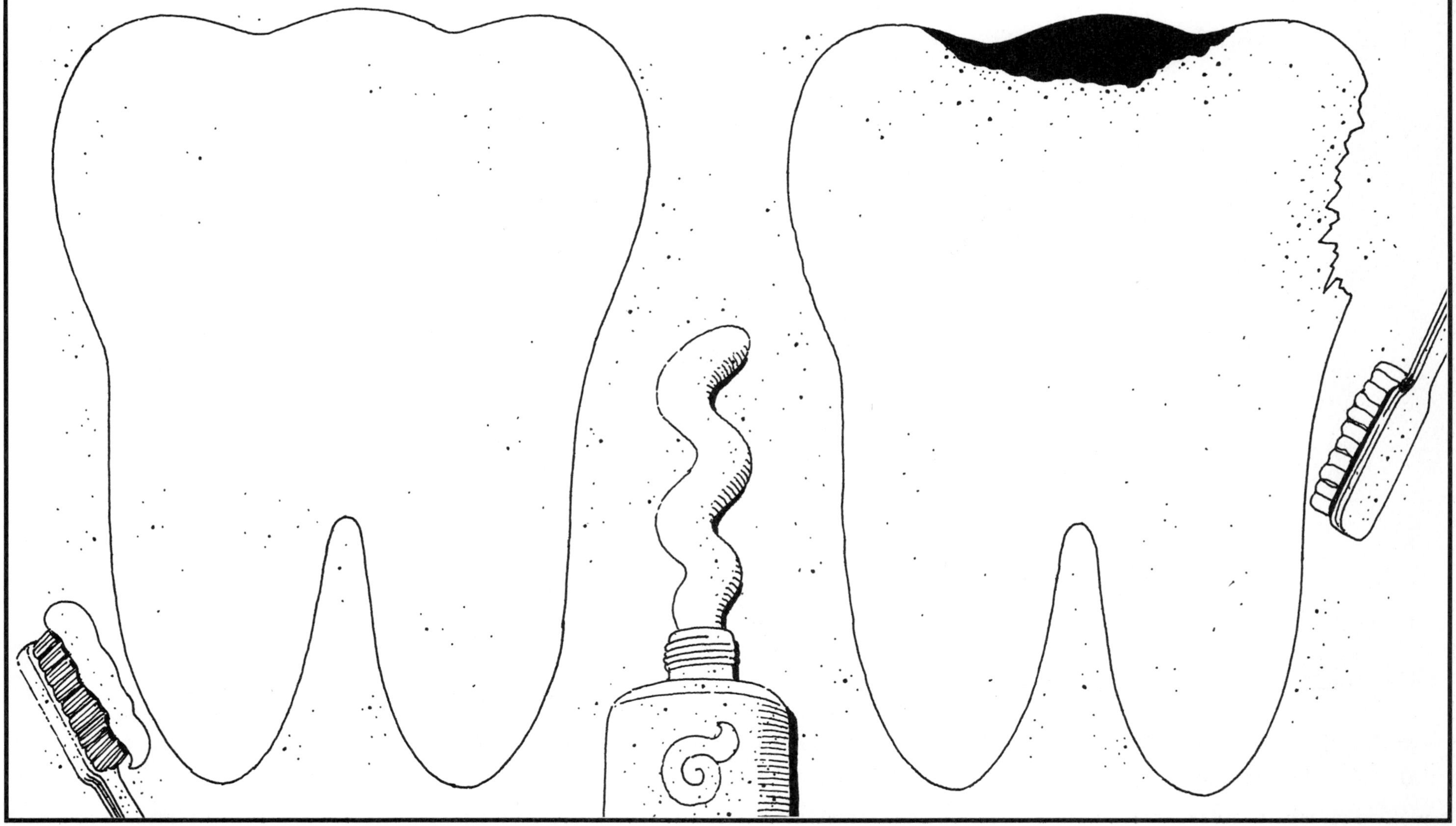

Name ____________________

Cups and beakers

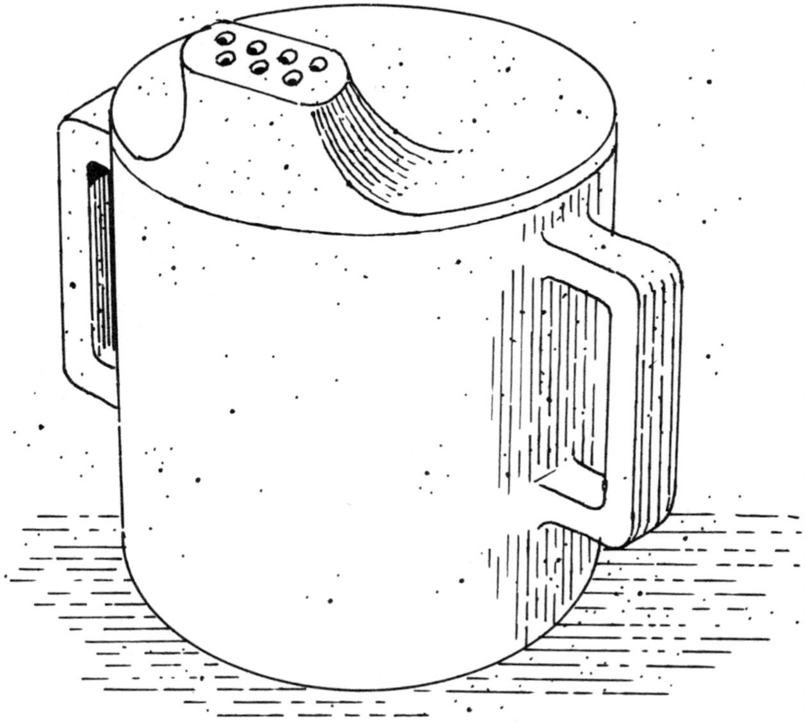

1 ______________________________ 1 ______________________________

2 ______________________________ 2 ______________________________

Here are two different cups.

- ✤ Under each cup write two drinks that might be drunk from it.
- ✤ Make a collection of different cups. Try to include ones which do a special job.
- ✤ Now fill in the cups and beakers chart.

Name ____________________

Cups and beakers chart

Picture of cup	What is it made from?	Is it reusable?	Will it break easily?	Is it easy to knock over?	With a hot drink in it, would it burn your hand?	What improvements could you make?

- ✤ Which cup would be best for serving cocoa at a bonfire party? Give your reasons.
- ✤ Ask your teacher for more copies of the chart if you need them.

Name ____________________

Flour carriers

Flour carriers

Both of these containers can be made using just one sheet of A4 paper, scissors and glue or sticky tape.

✤ Try making each one.
- Which holds more flour?
- How do you know?

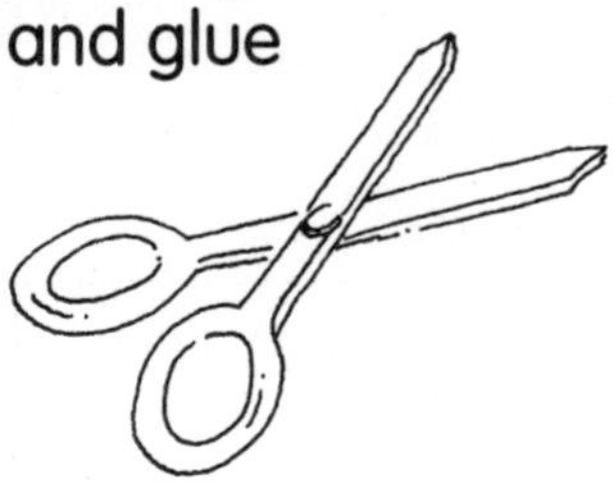

✤ Make two more different-shaped flour carriers, using just one A4 sheet of paper, scissors and glue or sticky tape for each.

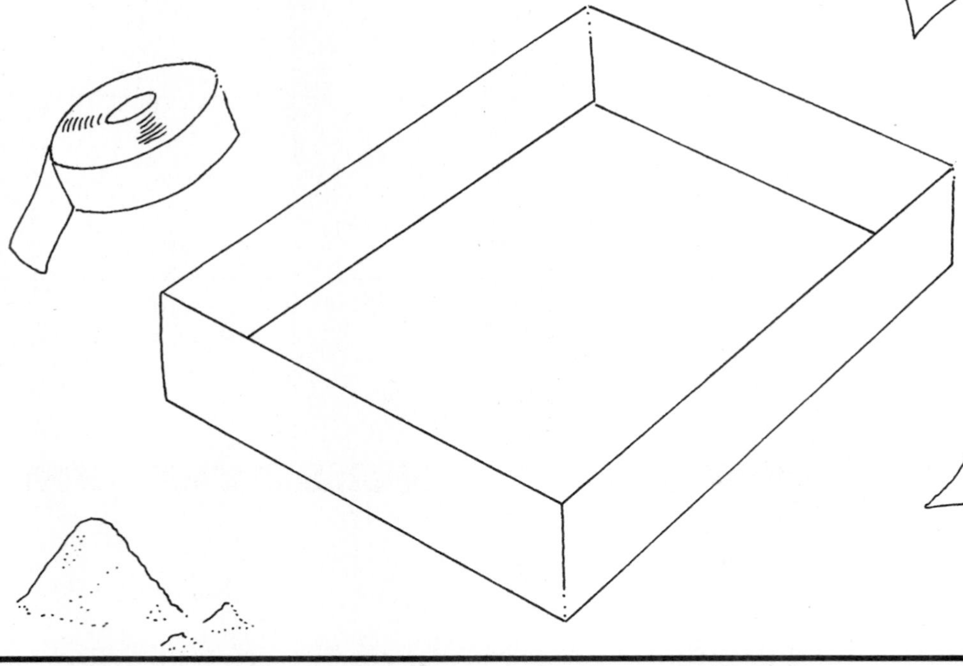

Boil an egg

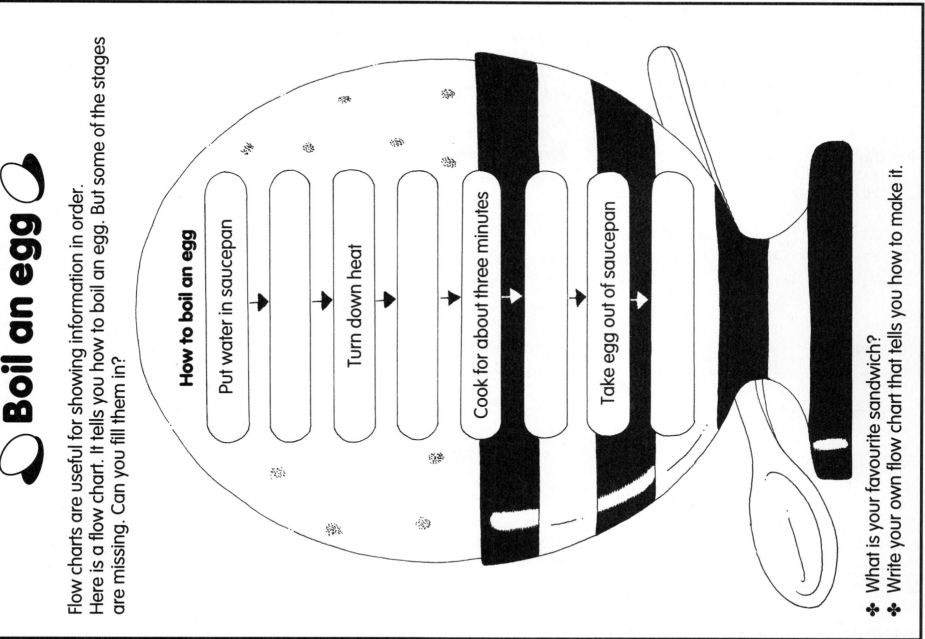

Flow charts are useful for showing information in order.
Here is a flow chart. It tells you how to boil an egg. But some of the stages are missing. Can you fill them in?

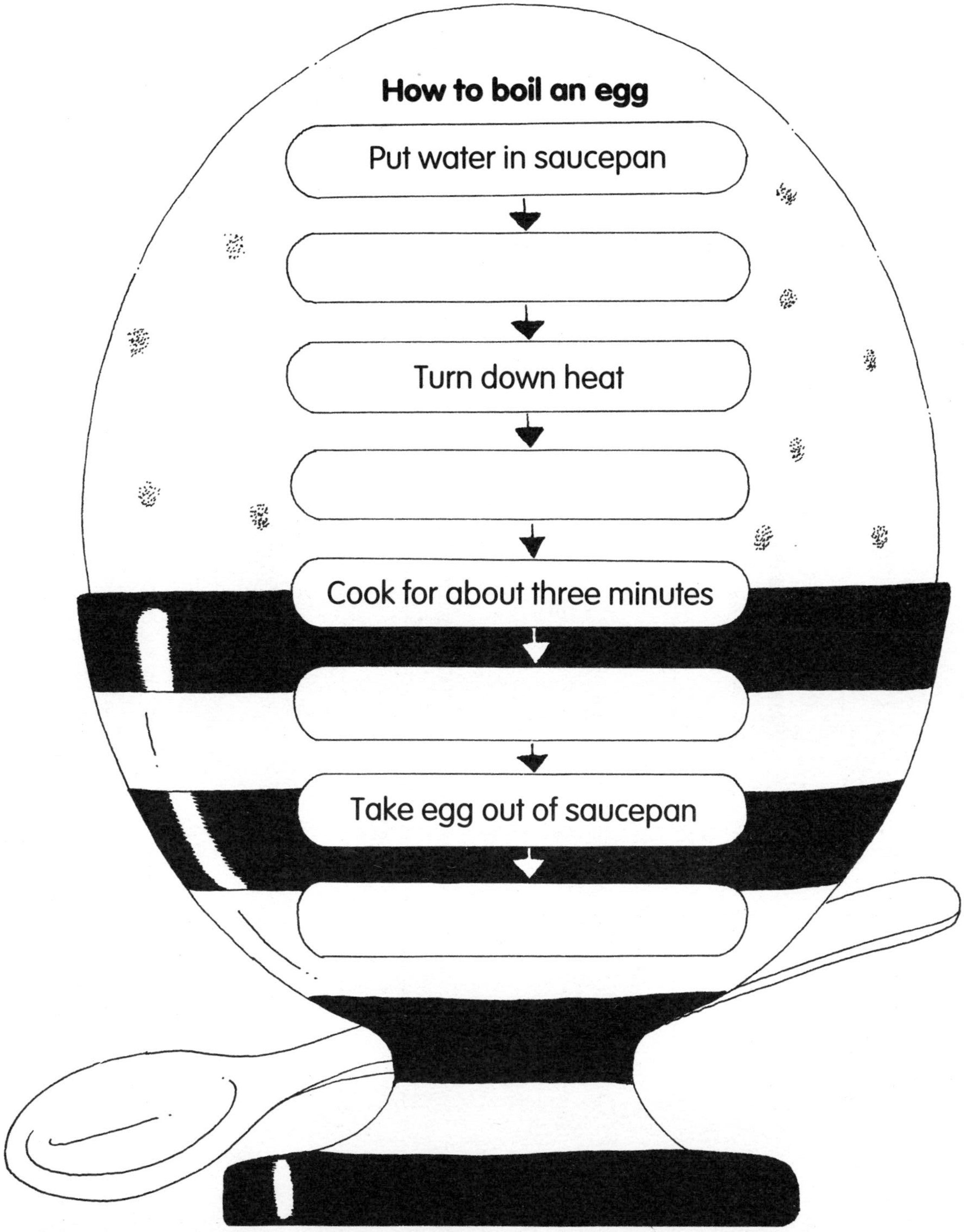
How to boil an egg
Put water in saucepan
Turn down heat
Cook for about three minutes
Take egg out of saucepan

- ✤ What is your favourite sandwich?
- ✤ Write your own flow chart that tells you how to make it.

Name ______________

Scrambled food

Scrambled food

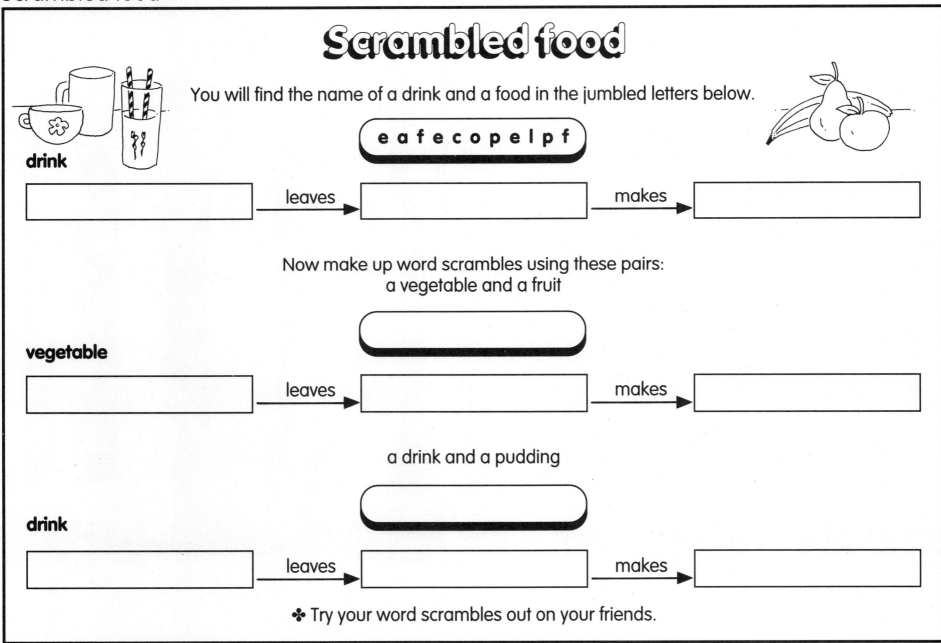

You will find the name of a drink and a food in the jumbled letters below.

e a f e c o p e l p f

drink

[ ] leaves → [ ] makes → [ ]

Now make up word scrambles using these pairs:
a vegetable and a fruit

[ ]

vegetable

[ ] leaves → [ ] makes → [ ]

a drink and a pudding

[ ]

drink

[ ] leaves → [ ] makes → [ ]

✤ Try your word scrambles out on your friends.

Name ____________________

Cooking apron

You need an apron for cooking. Would you choose any of these?
✤ For each one say why you would or would not choose it.

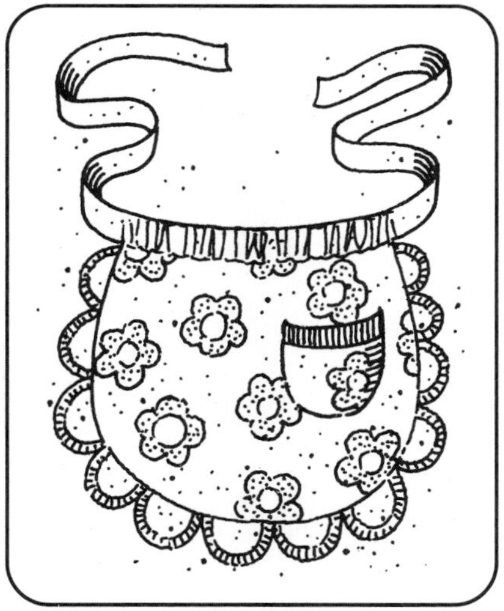

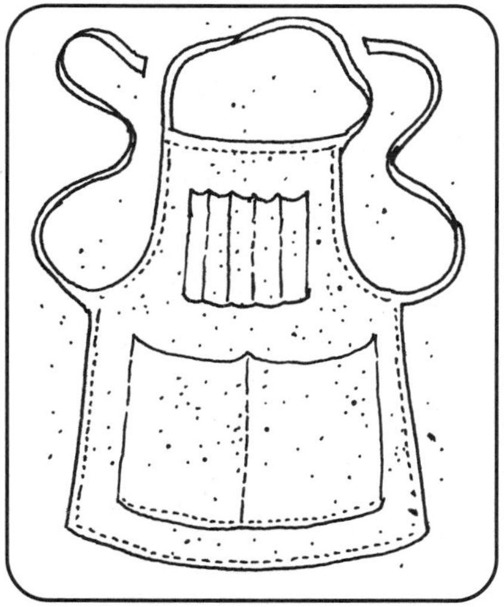

✤ Use the planning sheet to design and make a cooking apron that will fit you.

- What will it be made from?
- What shape will it be?
- How will you fasten it?

Name ______________

Grilled cheese sandwich

Grilled cheese sandwich

Below are the processes involved in making an open, grilled cheese sandwich:

✤ Number the processes in the correct sequence.

- ☐ Watch the bread and cheese until the cheese turns golden brown.
- ☐ Take a slice of bread.
- ☐ Eat the open sandwich.
- ☐ Put the bread and cheese combination under the grill.
- ☐ Turn on the grill.
- ☐ Place the grated cheese mix on top of the bread.
- ☐ Remove the bread and cheese from the heat.
- ☐ Add a sprinkle of pepper.

✤ Write out the recipe so that it could be understood by somebody who does not speak (or read) English.
How might you do this? Draw symbols? Take photos?
Can you think of any other ways?

Name ____________________

Special occasion cake

You are going to celebrate a special occasion. What will it be?

✤ Design a cake to suit the occasion. What shape will it be?
You can use these cake tins:

a square tin | a large round tin | a small round tin

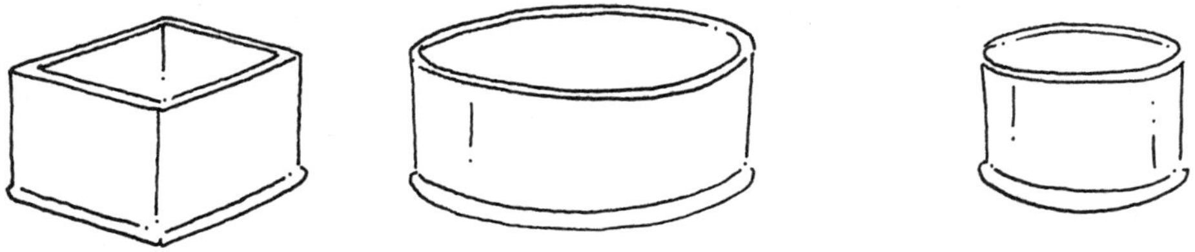

You can also use a swiss roll. You can cut out any shapes you may need from the cakes you have.

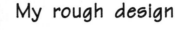

My rough design

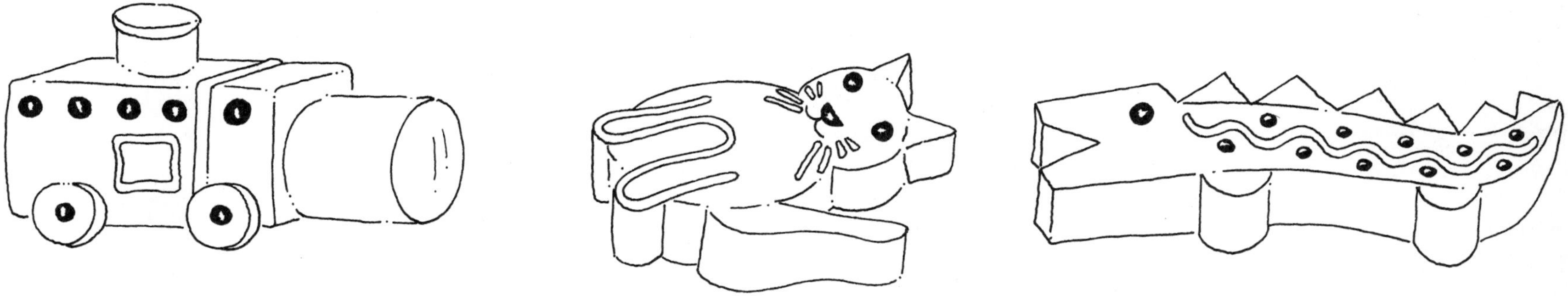

✤ How will the cake be decorated? Will you use sweets? Will there be a message on the cake?
✤ Use the planning sheet to draw a picture that shows how your cake should be made.
✤ Write labels that explain exactly what should be done.

Name ____________________

Carrier bag

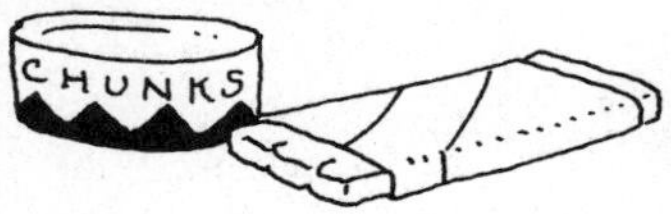

Carrier bag

Food shops often give customers a carrier bag to hold their shopping.

- Make a collection of different carrier bags. Look at how each one is made.
- Choose four different types of carrier bag. Draw and label each one.

Think about handles, materials and shape.

1

2

3

4

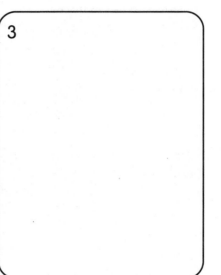

- Which bag is the strongest? Think of a test to find out.
- Use the testing sheet to record your results.
- Design a carrier bag strong enough to carry the weight of six cans of soft drink.

What material will you use? How will you fix it together? How can you make it strong? Think about handles and the base. Use the planning sheet.

- Make and test your bag. Did it hold the weight of the cans?

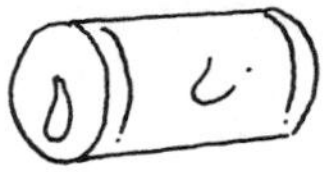

Make a wordsearch

✤ Devise a wordsearch all about food and drink. You must include 20 words.
✤ Write your list here in pencil, so that you can rub them out later.
✤ Make sure you use either all capital letters or all small letters. Check your spelling!

My list

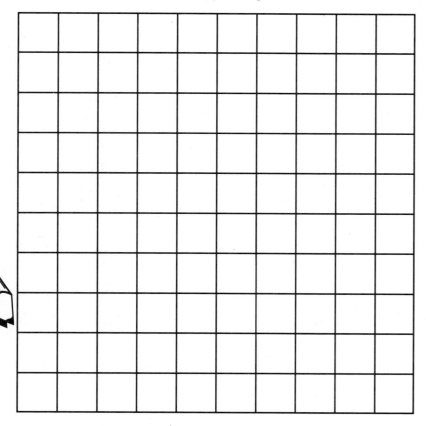

1 ____________	11 ____________
2 ____________	12 ____________
3 ____________	13 ____________
4 ____________	14 ____________
5 ____________	15 ____________
6 ____________	16 ____________
7 ____________	17 ____________
8 ____________	18 ____________
9 ____________	19 ____________
10 ____________	20 ____________

✤ When you have finished, make a note of your words on another piece of paper. Rub out your words written on the list above and try out your puzzle on a friend.

Name ___________________

Tudor cooking device

Tudor cooking device

In Tudor times people cooked over an open fire. They could not turn the heat up and down like we can on a modern cooker. How could they stop the food from burning?

✤ Write your ideas here.

My ideas

✤ Choose one type of food.

✤ Use the planning sheet to design and make a model of a device which would allow the food to be cooked without burning.

Name ____________________

posy mat

In rich 16th century households, dinner ended with a sticky pudding or sweetmeats, such as marchpane (marzipan). The sweet was served on posy mats. These were thin, round pottery mats glazed with tin and decorated on one side with flower patterns and an amusing verse. The food was eaten from the plain side and after the meal the guest turned over the mat to read the message.

✤ Design and make your own posy mat. Use this page to plan your design.

Name ________________

Banana sweet dish

Banana sweet dish

- You have been challenged to make a sweet dish for yourself and a friend using bananas as the main ingredient.
- Work with a partner. Write down the problems you need to think about before you start. Consider what ingredients you will use, how much it will cost and so on.

Problems:

- Use the chart below to draw up a plan of your dish. Write its name in the space at the top.

Ingredient					
Amount of the ingredient needed					
Cost of the ingredient	Estimate / Actual cost	Estimate / Actual cost	Estimate / Actual cost	Estimate / Actual cost	Estimate / Actual cost
Processes to be used					
Tools/utensils needed					

Name ____________________

Improve the system

✤ Carry out a study of your school dining area during lunch-time. Look at how the food is served and then cleared away.

✤ Think of ways to make the system better. Could it be simpler? Could it be quicker? How?

✤ Draw and write what was wrong with the system and give your ideas for improvements.

What I saw that was wrong

My ideas for improvement

Name ______________

Food boxes

Food boxes

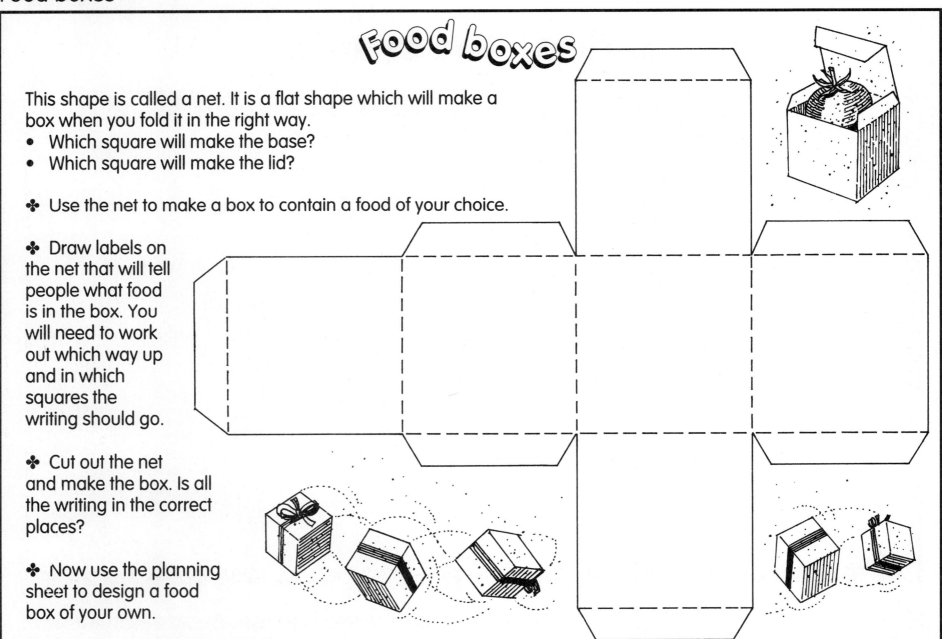

This shape is called a net. It is a flat shape which will make a box when you fold it in the right way.

- Which square will make the base?
- Which square will make the lid?

✤ Use the net to make a box to contain a food of your choice.

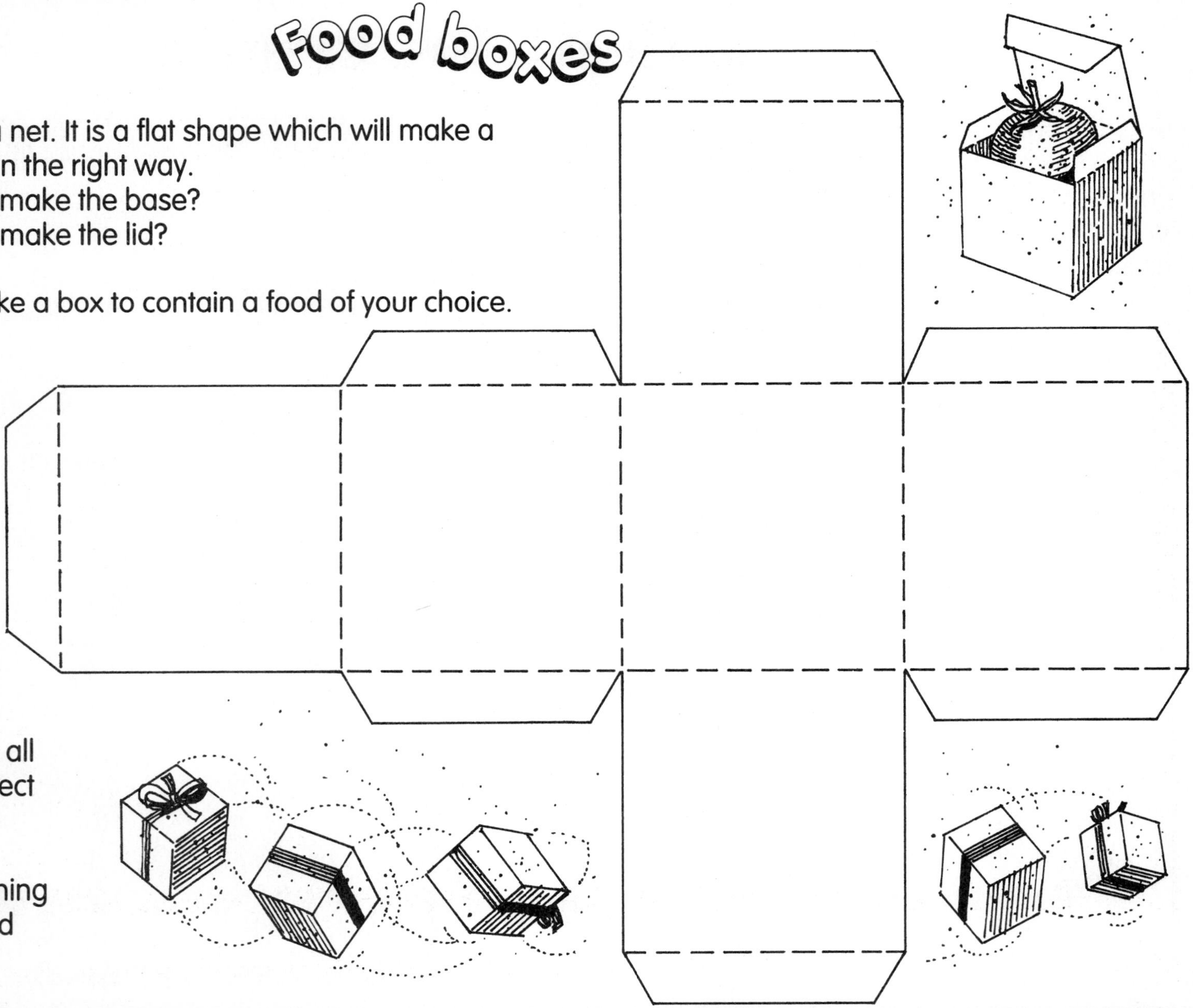

✤ Draw labels on the net that will tell people what food is in the box. You will need to work out which way up and in which squares the writing should go.

✤ Cut out the net and make the box. Is all the writing in the correct places?

✤ Now use the planning sheet to design a food box of your own.

Name ____________________

Make a shaduf

The Ancient Egyptian farmers planted food crops in the fields alongside the banks of the River Nile.
In the season when the Nile did not flood they had to water their fields. They lifted the water from the river or a storage canal by using a shaduf.

✤ Think of some present day uses for the shaduf idea.

My ideas

✤ Design and make a model shaduf that will lift a load up, swing it round and lower it.

Name ____________________

Cover story

Cover story

✤ Help the author by putting a design on this blank book cover.
✤ Look at some books in your classroom or library. What else is needed as well as a picture?

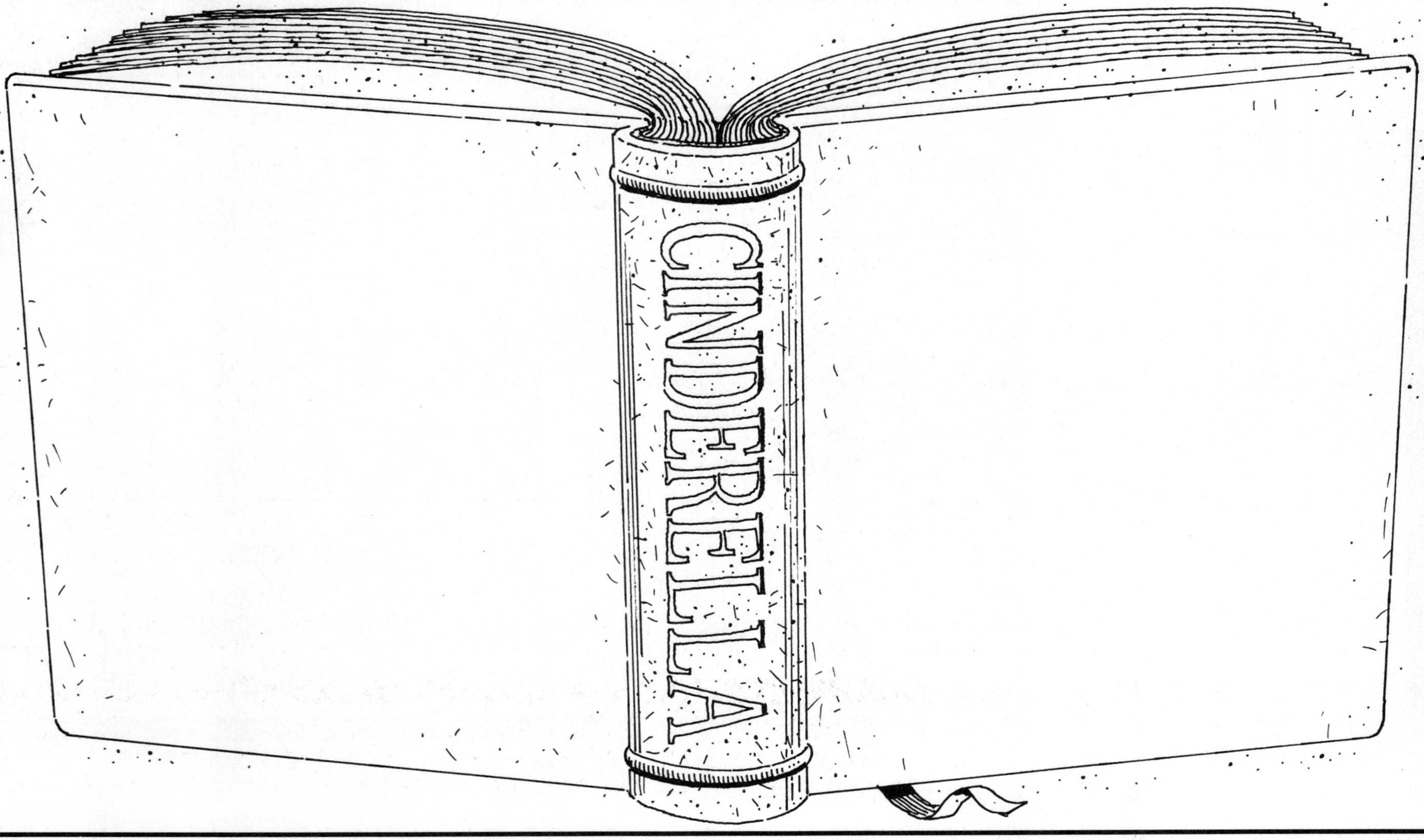

Save ! Sam

Sam the lighthouse-keeper is trapped in his lighthouse.
The door is stuck fast and he cannot open it.

✤ Think of four ways to rescue him from the lighthouse.

1
2
3
4

✤ Choose one of your ideas and use it in a story.

Name ____________________

Special colour

Tigers are coloured so that they seem to fade away in their natural surroundings. Can you think why?

- ✤ Colour this tiger outline. What colours will you use?
- ✤ Now cut out the tiger. Make a background for your tiger to hide in.
- ✤ Can you think of other animals that use colour to hide themselves?

Name ____________________

Eyes tell a story

Eyes can often tell us about how someone is feeling.

✤ Use these eyes to make Gary Gorilla look:

- happy
- cross
- sad
- puzzled

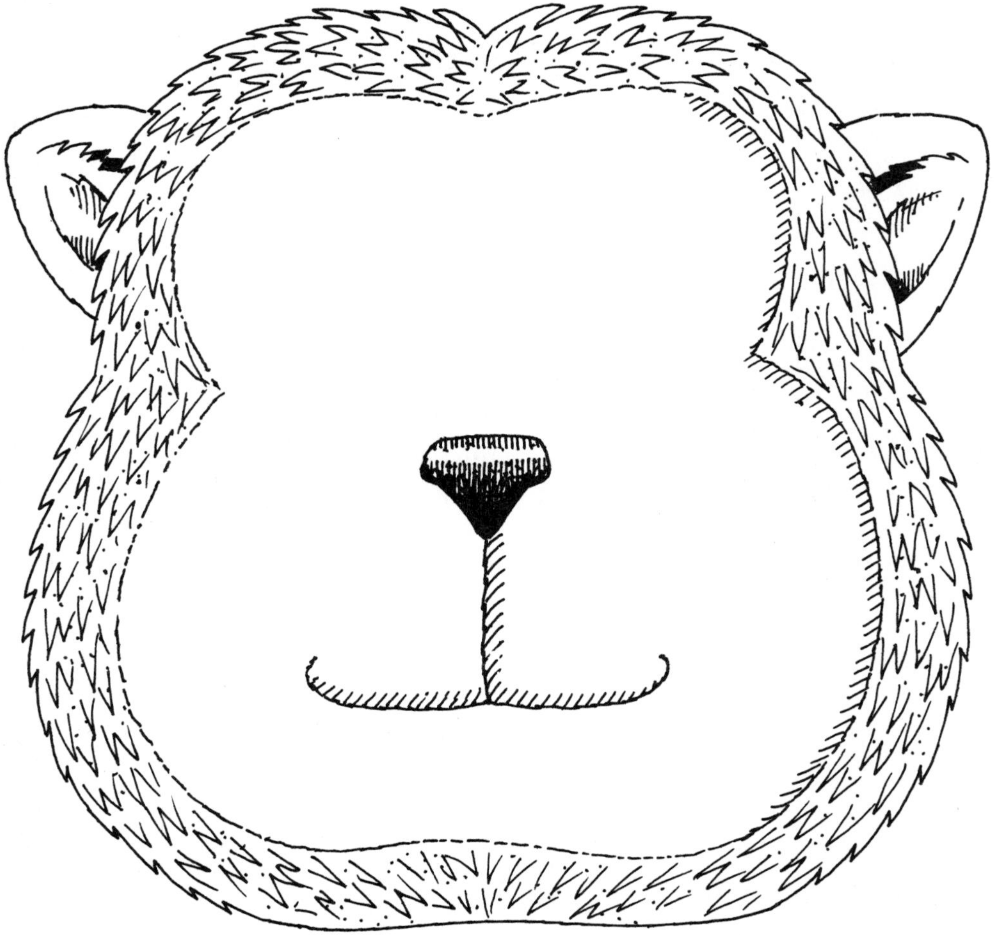

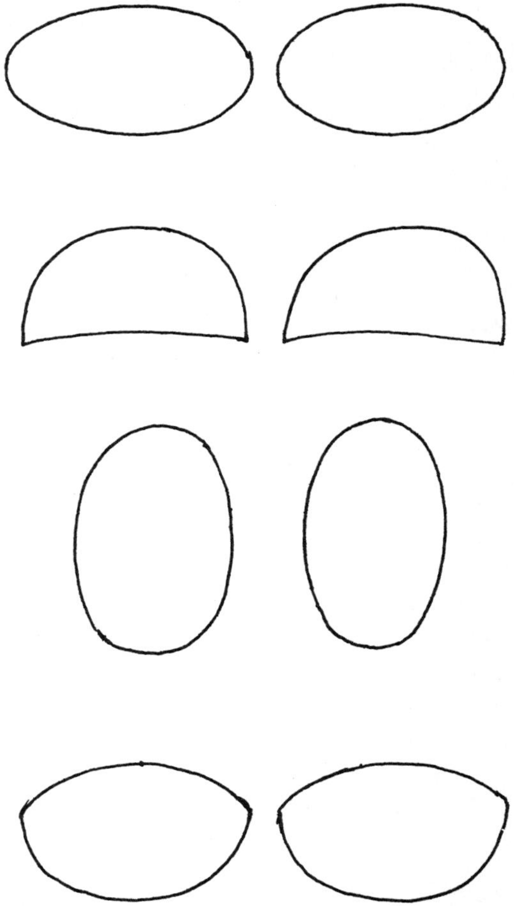

✤ Write a story about why Gary Gorilla feels sad.

Name ____________________

Creating harmony

✤ Find a picture of a rainbow. We say the colours next to each other are in harmony. They work together to give a peaceful effect.

✤ Choose two colours for this stripy pattern. Use them to create harmony.

✤ Choose two different colours. Create harmony in this circle.

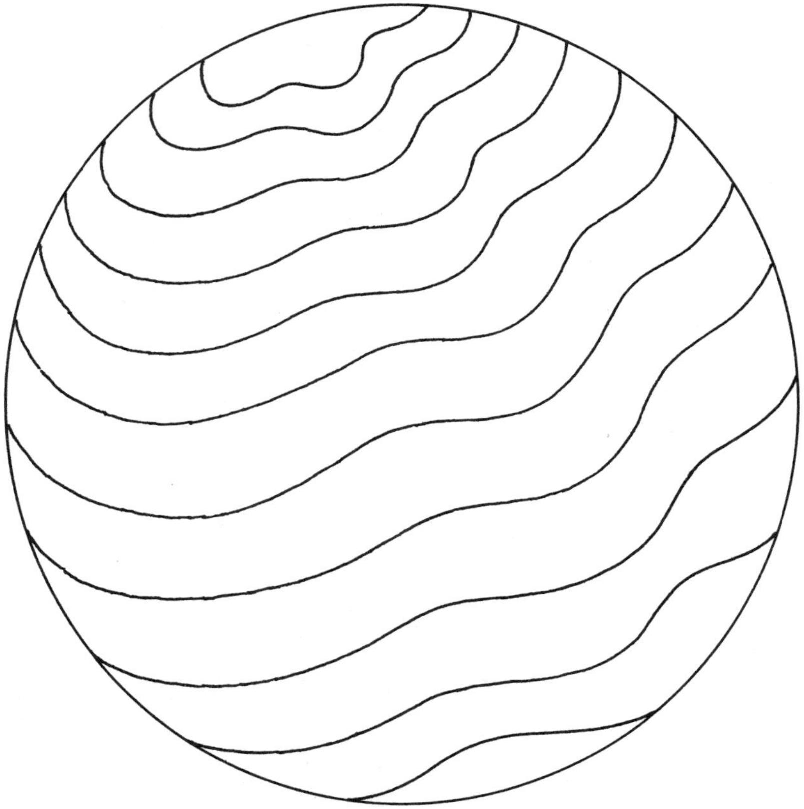

Name ____________________

Weather report

Here are some weather symbols.

cloudy

sunny

raining

partly cloudy

✤ Think of some symbols to show windy weather and a thunderstorm.
✤ Draw them in the empty boxes.

✤ Cut out all of the symbols.
✤ Design and make a weather chart that uses your symbols.
✤ Decide whether you want to use colour.

Name ____________________

Mirror, mirror

Mirror, mirror

Here is a mirror message. Can you read it?

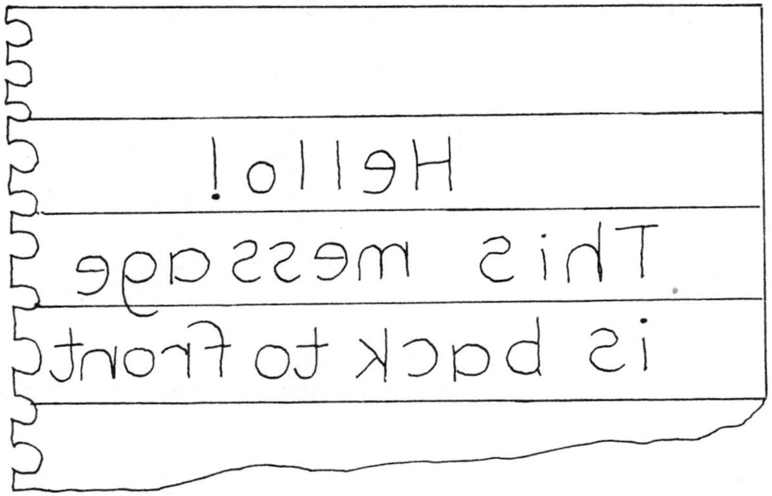

✤ Now work out what this mirror message says.

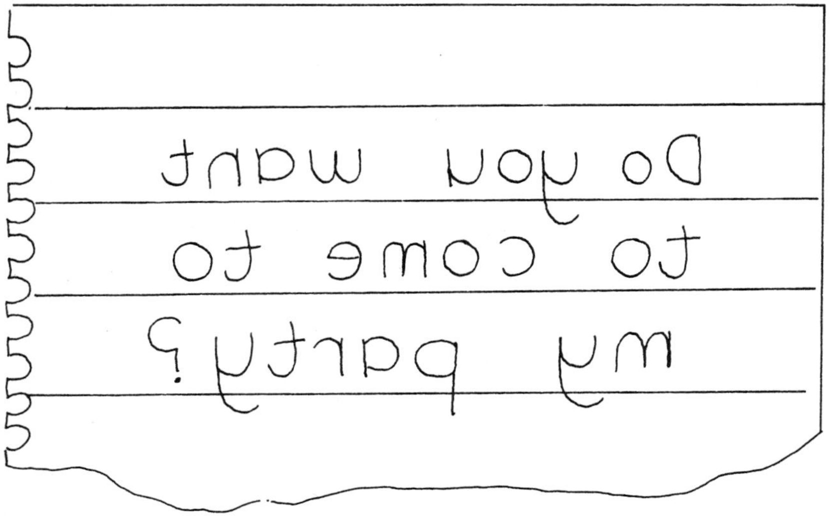

✤ Write what it says here.

✤ Write what it says here.

✤ Write your own message so that your friend can read it with a mirror.

Name ____________________

Ways of creating

Here is a picture of a tree.

✤ Think of six different techniques you could use to make the picture. In each box write the name of a technique.

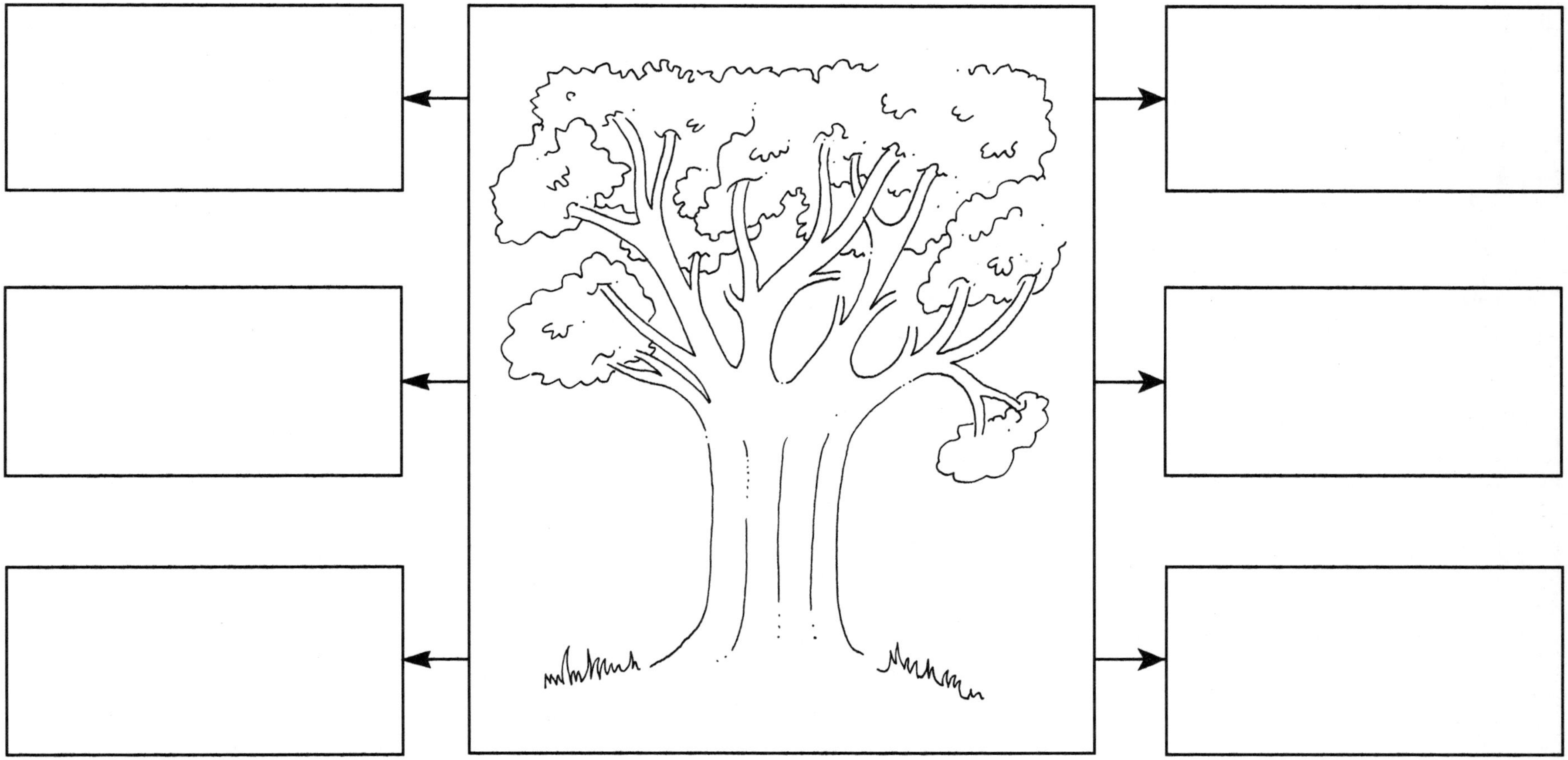

✤ Now try out your ideas. Do some of them work better than others?

✤ Did you think of blowing paint or printing? If not, try them.

Butterfly life cycle

The butterfly has four main stages in its life cycle. Here are the stages.

- Cut them out and put them in the correct order.
- Write down what each stage is.

____

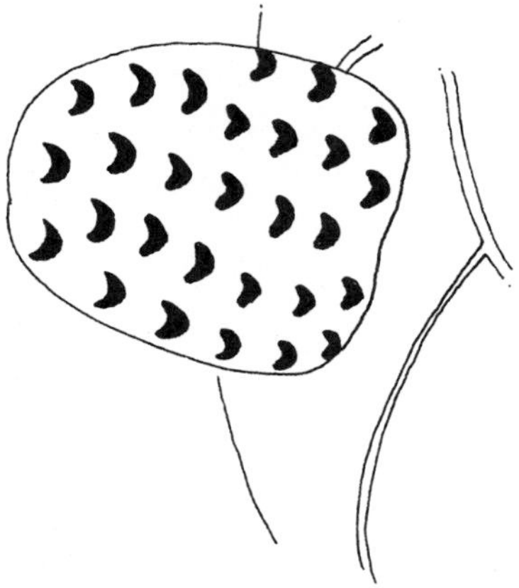

____

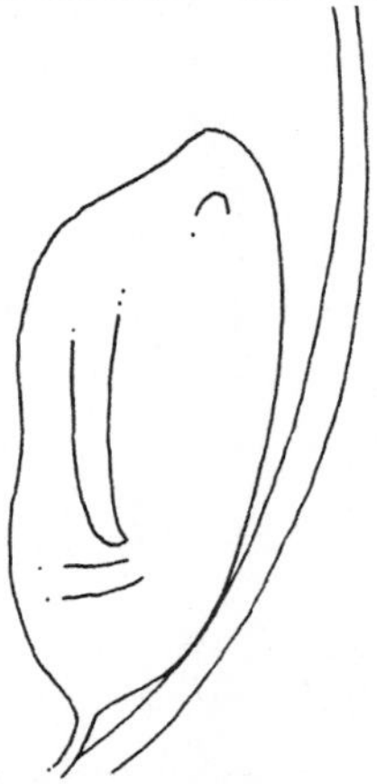

____

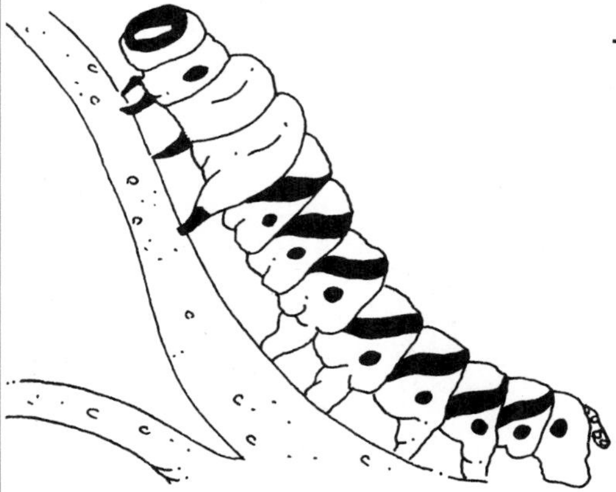

____

- Now write a caption for each picture. Try not to use more than ten words for each caption.

Stop press!

Here is a headline from the Mothergooseville Daily News. Can you guess which nursery rhyme it relates to?

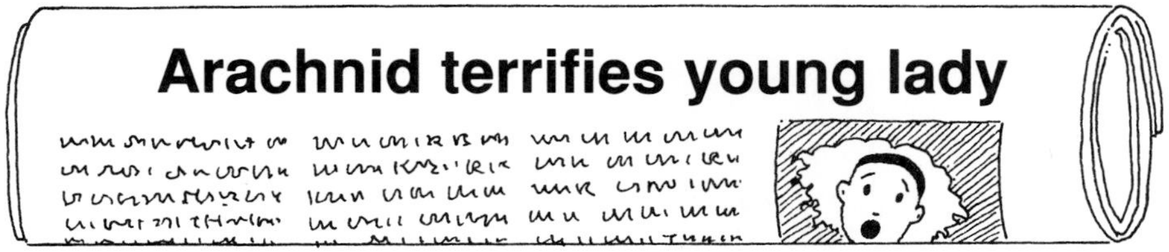
Arachnid terrifies young lady

✤ Write a newspaper headline for these two nursery rhymes. Use no more than five words for each.

Mothergooseville Daily News

Humpty Dumpty sat on a wall.
Humpty Dumpty had a great fall.
All the King's horses and all the King's men,
couldn't put Humpty together again.

Mothergooseville Daily News

Jack and Jill went up the hill,
to fetch a pail of water.
Jack fell down and broke his crown and
Jill came tumbling after.

✤ Write a short press report for each headline.

Name ____________________

Symbols

Symbols

Here are six sets of symbols.
✤ Write down what each set stands for.

✤ Add two more symbols to each set.
✤ Draw two different sets of symbols.

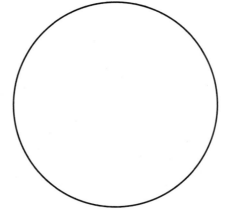

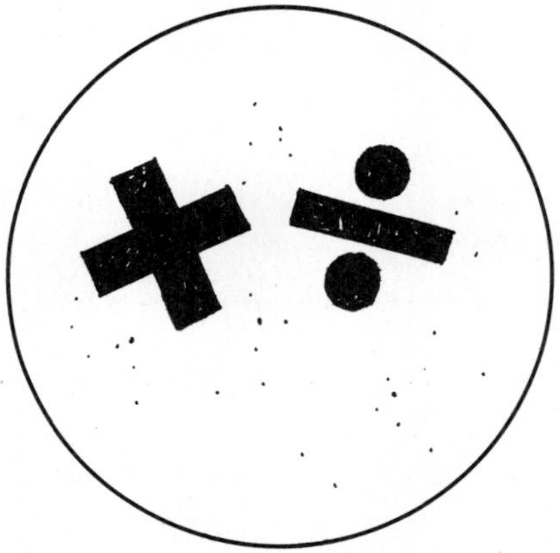

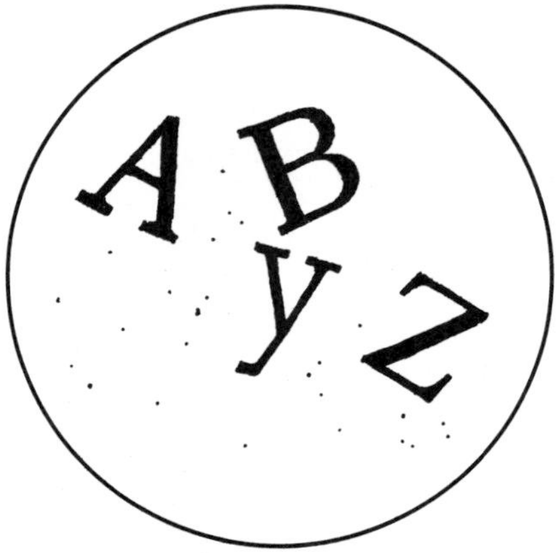

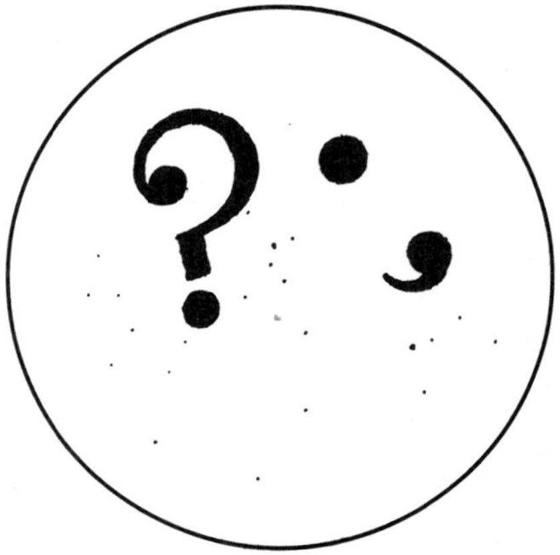

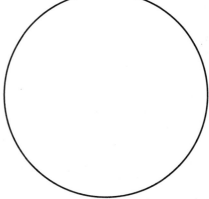

Roman numerals

II = 2 I = 1 XXX = 30 XL = 40

III = 3 L = 50

The Romans wrote their numbers in a different way from us. Look at the Roman numerals around the page.

IV = 4 LX = 60

- ✤ Write your age in Roman numerals. ____________
- ✤ Write the number of children in your class today in Roman numerals. ____________
- ✤ Fill in the gaps on these tablets.

V = 5 LXX = 70

VI = 6 LXXX = 80

VII = 7 XC = 90

VIII = 8 C = 100

IX = 9 CC = 200

X = 10 CCC = 300

XI = 11 CD = 400

XII = 12 D = 500

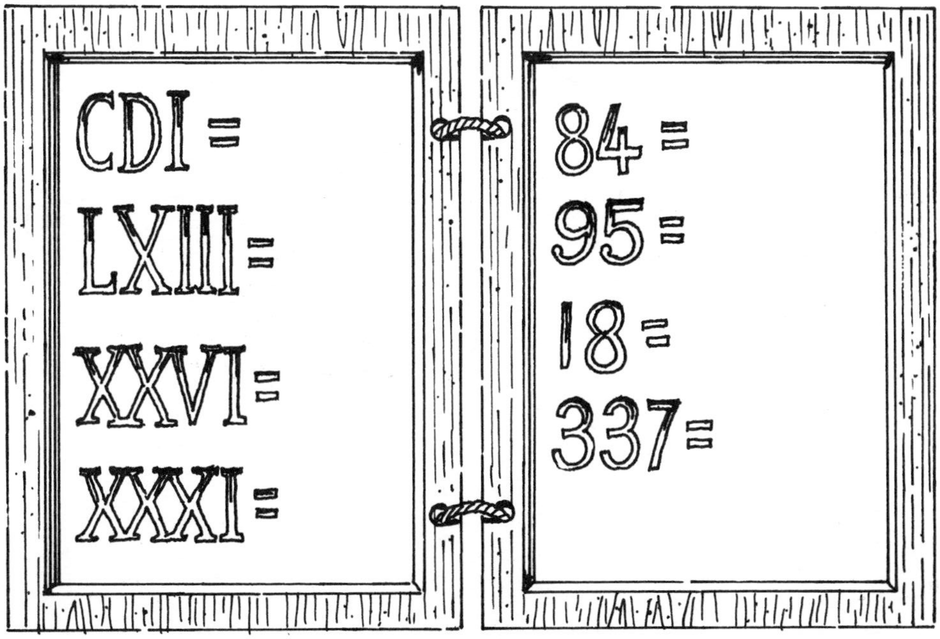

Try writing your birthday and tomorrow's date in Roman numerals on these tablets.

XIII = 13 DC = 600

XIV = 14 DCC = 700

XV = 15 DCCC = 800

XVI = 16 CM = 900

XVII = 17 M = 1000

XVIII = 18

XIX = 19

XX = 20 MM = 2000

Name ____________________

What's the clue?

What's the clue

Here is a completed crossword. The theme is giants.

- ✤ Write the clues for it.
- ✤ Use the grid paper to make a blank crossword.
- ✤ Give your clues to a friend. Can he or she fill in the empty puzzle?

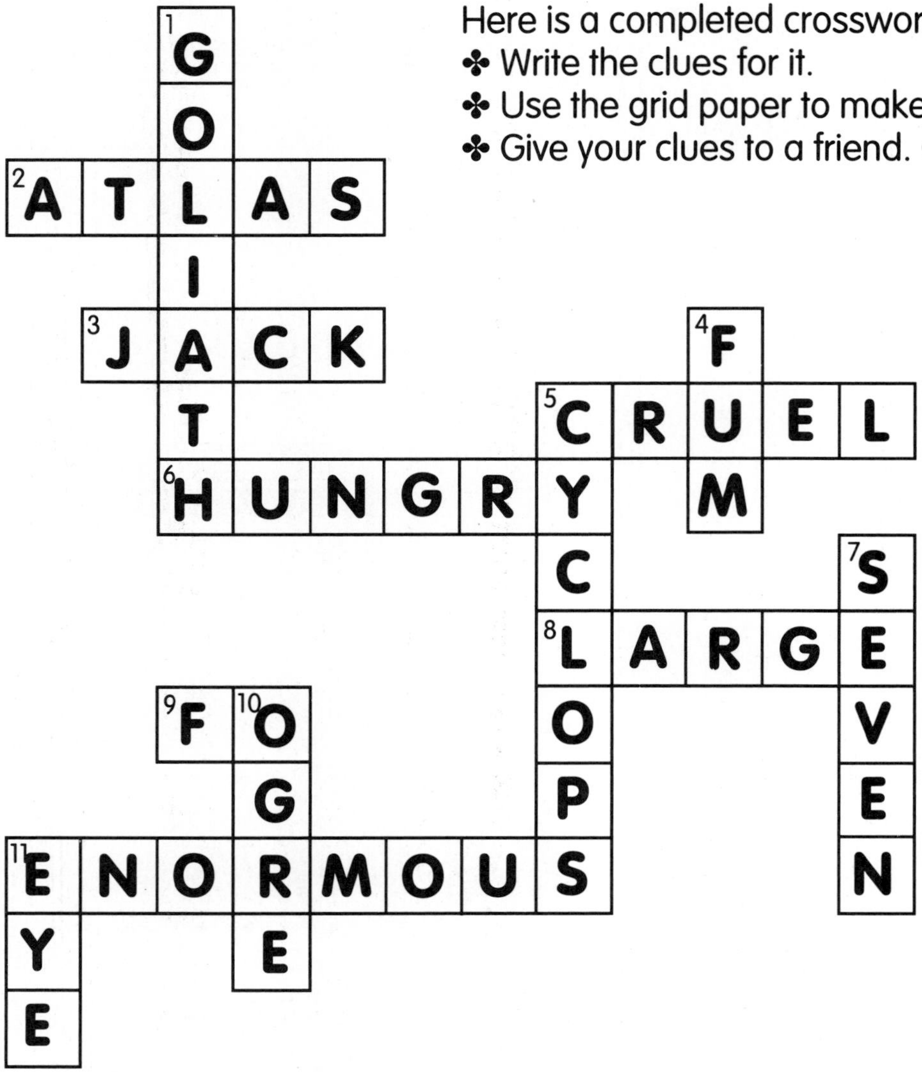

Across

2 ____________________

3 ____________________

5 ____________________

6 ____________________

8 ____________________

9 ____________________

11 ____________________

Down

1 ____________________

4 ____________________

5 ____________________

7 ____________________

10 ____________________

11 ____________________

Make a map

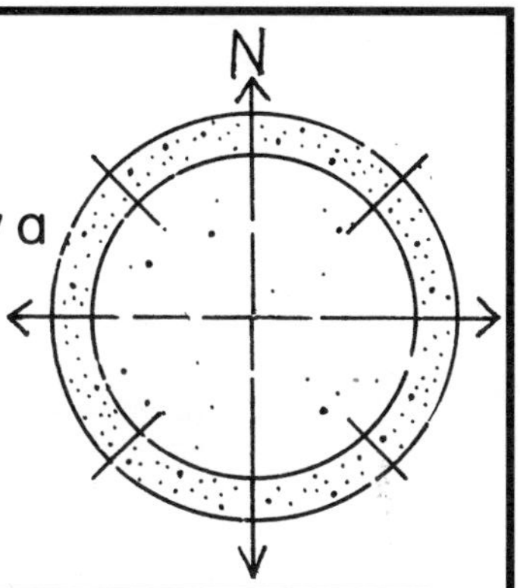

✤ Use the information at the bottom of this page to draw a map of Greenville. Use a scale of 1cm equals 1km.
You can use a direction compass or protractor.
(Hint: start in the middle of a blank A4 sheet.)
You could use this key or make up your own.

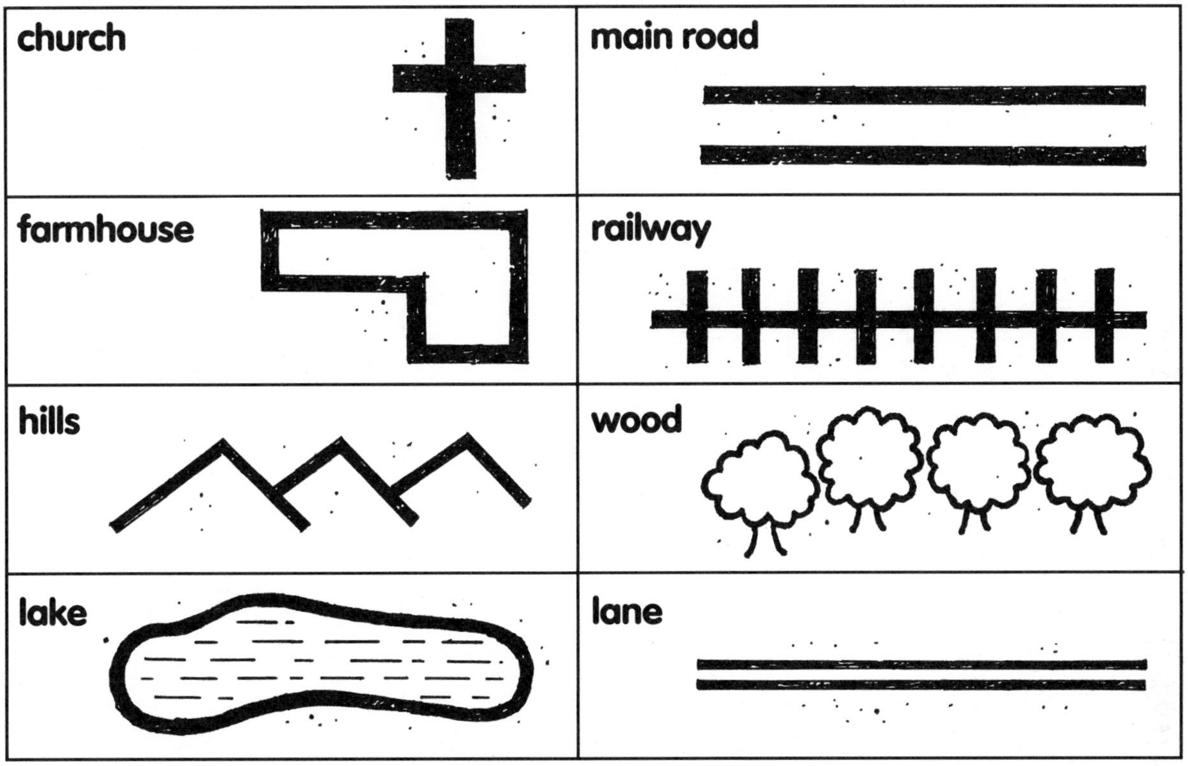

- In the centre of Greenville there is a church.
- 6km north is a main road. It runs from west to east.
- A railway runs along the north side of the main road.
- A lane runs due south from the main road to the church.
- 5km south of the church is a lake.
- 2km south-east of the church is a farmhouse.
- 2km south of this farmhouse are some hills.
- There is a wood 6km west of the hills.

Name ____________________

Why write?

Why write?

Here are four uses for writing:

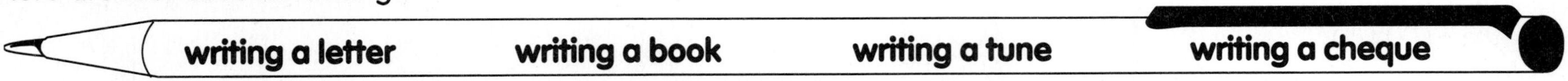

Think about their similarities and differences. Choose two to compare. Record your ideas on the chart.

	letter	book	tune	cheque
similarities				
differences				

Code wheel

✤ Cut out the two wheels and glue them on to thin card.
✤ Cut around each one.
✤ Fasten the smaller wheel on to the larger one so that it will spin round.

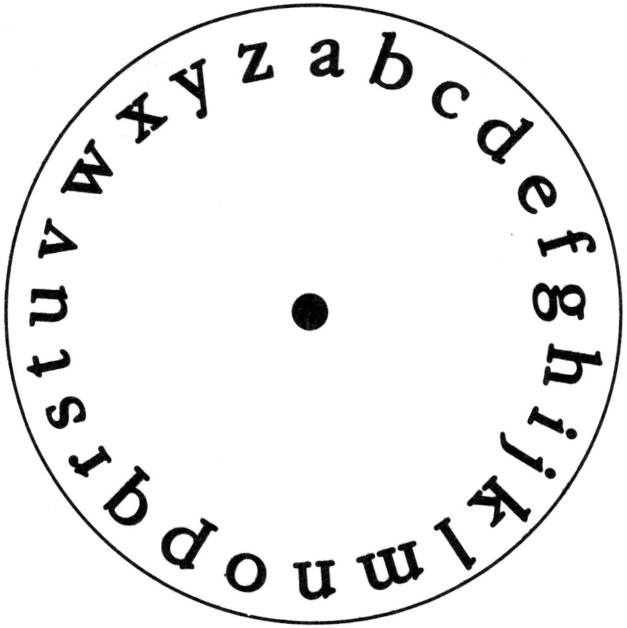

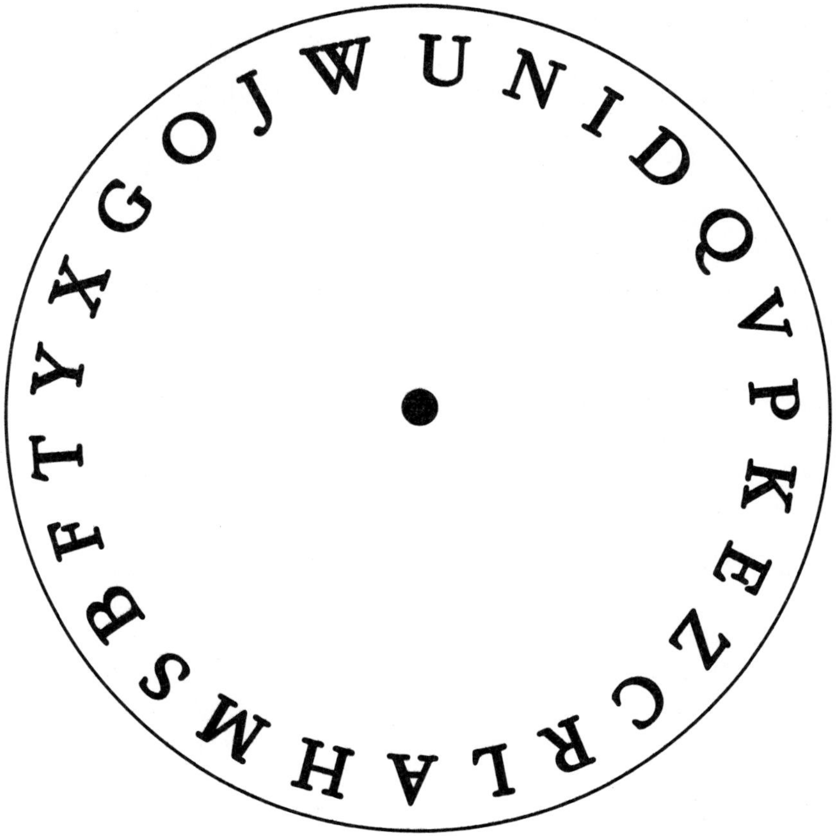

✤ To write a message put the small 'a' opposite any capital letter on the outside wheel. Keep the wheel in the same place and change each letter of your message for the one opposite it on the outer wheel.
✤ Write a secret message to your friend. You will need to think of a way to tell him or her what code you are using.
✤ Devise another code in a similar way.

Message carrier

✤ Make up a message and send it to your friend in the classroom next door. You don't want everyone to know what your message says, so you need to write it in code form.

✤ Make up your code here.

✤ Write your message here.

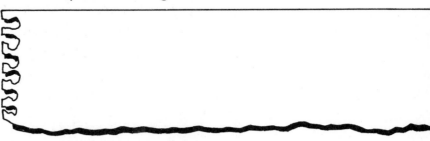

✤ Now encode your message.

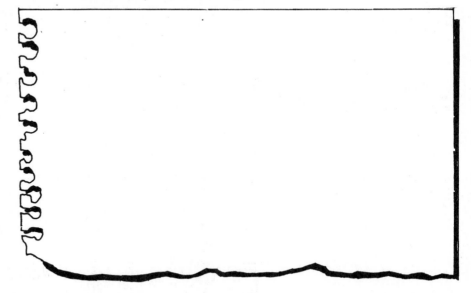

✤ Design and make something that will carry the message from your classroom to the one next door. Use the planning sheet to help you.

Name ____________________

Light signals

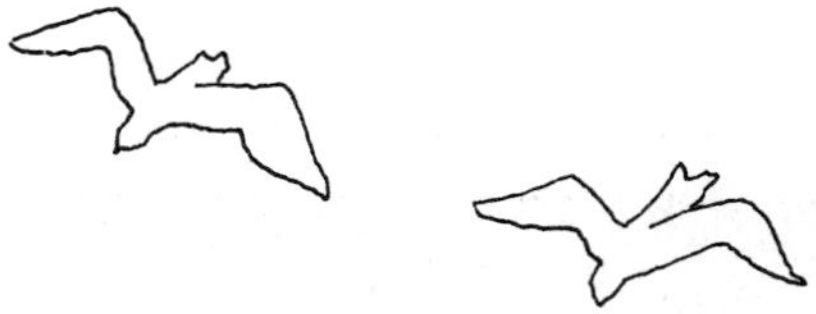

Lights are often used to send messages - lighthouses are an example.

✤ On the sheet below, write down other ways of using light to send messages.

✤ Think of a message you need to send. How could you send the message by light?

✤ Use the planning sheet to design and make the device you thought of for sending the message.

My list

Name ____________________

Tudor shop sign

Tudor shop sign

In Tudor times not everybody could read, so shop signs had symbols on to show people what went on inside.

- ✤ Imagine that you are a shopkeeper in those days. What type of shop will you have?
- ✤ Make a list of ideas associated with your shop. Draw the symbols for them.

idea	symbol

- ✤ Design and make a pictorial shop sign to advertise your business. Your sign must be able to be hung up.
- ✤ Do some rough sketches with labels below. Which sign works best? Discuss this with someone.

- ✤ Choose the best design for your sign. Use the planning sheet to work out the details.

Signs and symbols

The symbols shown here are easily understood. They are simple and easy to make.

✤ Make a list of ideas you could communicate to people in your school. Can each message be communicated without using words?

✤ Design some symbols for use in school. They might be for directing children, labelling doors or encouraging people not to do certain things.

My list

Name ________________

Nursery rhyme tape

Nursery rhyme tape

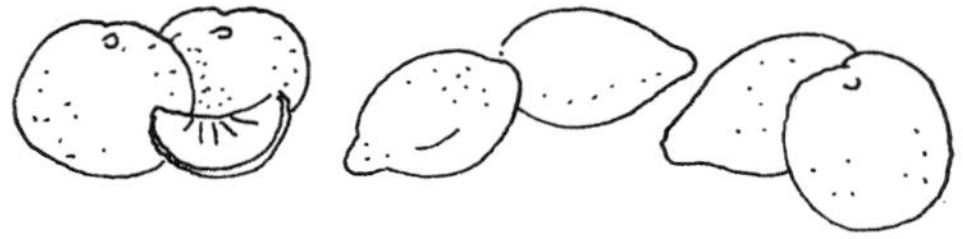

Make a five-minute nursery rhyme tape for young children on the theme of food.

✤ Think of some nursery rhymes. Which ones will you include? What about the order? Will the rhymes be sung or spoken? What about music?

✤ When you have made your tape, design a tape box card insert for it. Use the layout below to help you. What information should you include? Think about the title, the picture, the lettering.

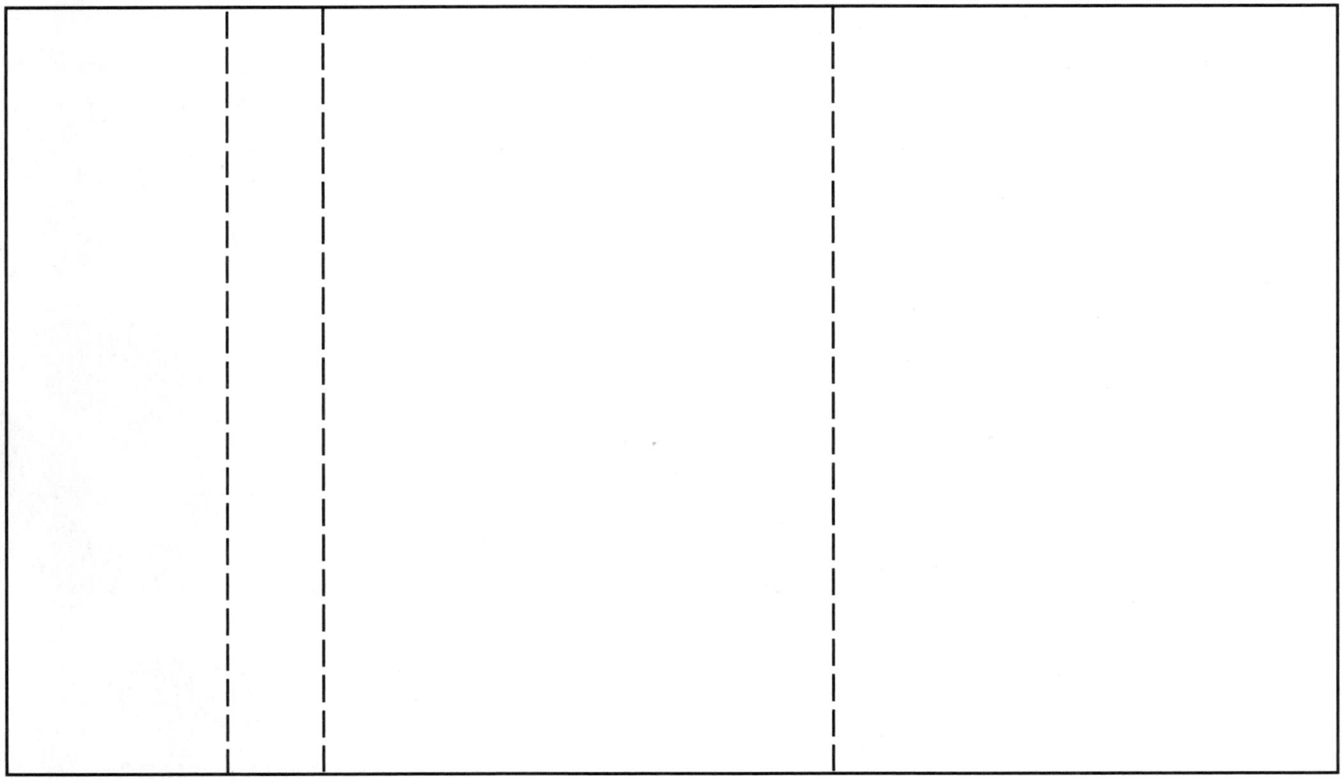

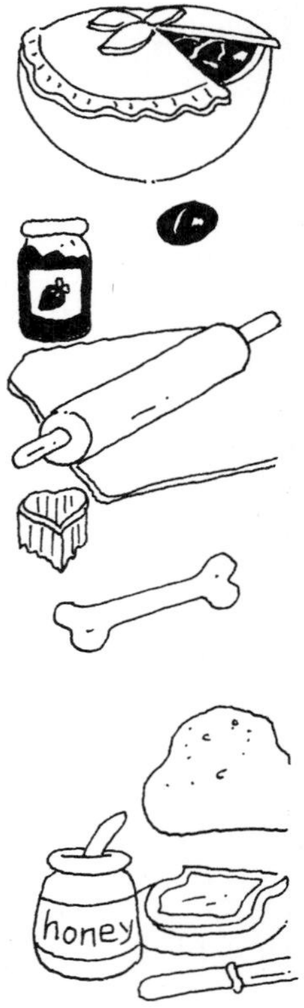

Name ____________________

Make do and mend

During World War II, few new things were made, so many everyday items, even soap and water, were in short supply. Since household items could not be replaced, 'make do and mend' was the only answer.

Newspapers, magazines and posters all showed the types of things people were expected to try.

Hints included: care and repair of shoes
new clothes from old
making soap last longer

✤ Plan a government campaign encouraging people not to waste anything.

- How will your message reach people?
- What form will your ideas take?
- Who will you need to contact to help you?
- Who is responsible for each stage?

✤ Think of a catchy slogan for your campaign.

✤ Think of ways other than newspapers, magazines and posters to tell people about your ideas.

My plan

My slogan

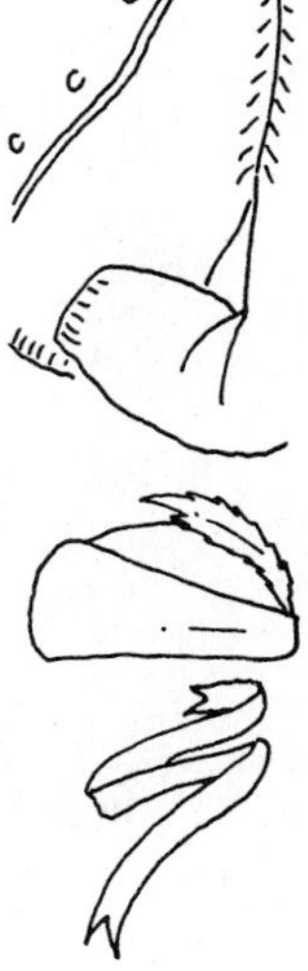

Name ____________________

Types of travel

✤ Under each picture write the name of the vehicle.

____________ ____________ ____________ ____________

____________ ____________ ____________ ____________

✤ Find out how many children in your class have travelled on each of these.

Type of vehicle	Number of children

✤ Draw a graph of your findings on a separate sheet of paper.

Name ____________________

Round and round

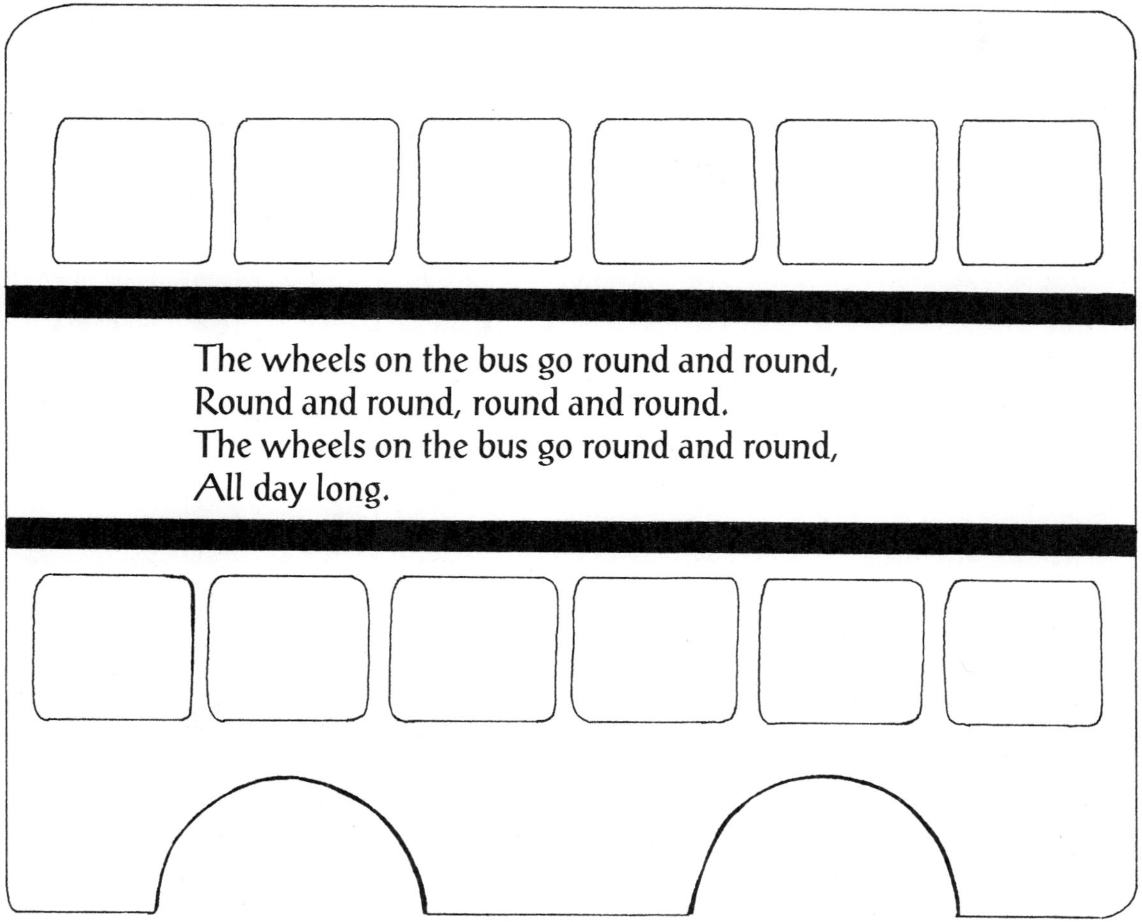

The wheels on the bus go round and round,
Round and round, round and round.
The wheels on the bus go round and round,
All day long.

✤ Use this outline to design and make a model of a bus with wheels that go round and round.
✤ How will people know where the bus is going?
✤ Write the information on the destination board.

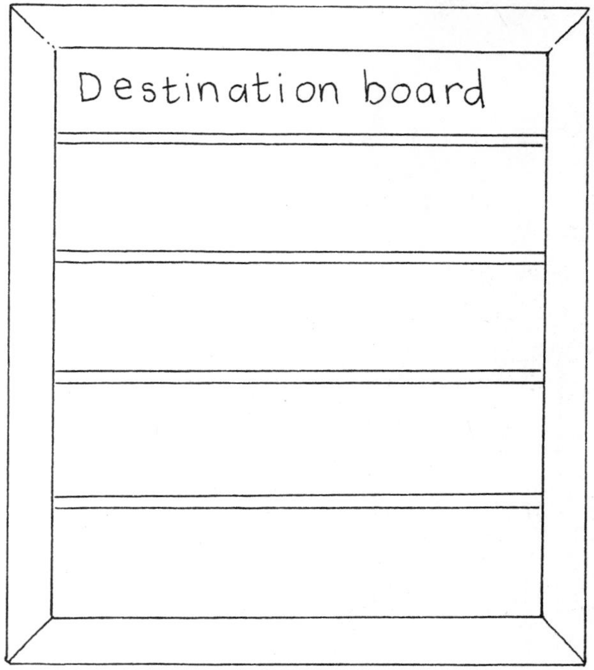

Name ______________________

Fire! Fire!

Fire! Fire!

✤ Make an extending ladder from the fire engine to reach Ted.

✤ What materials will you use? Use the planning sheet to help you.

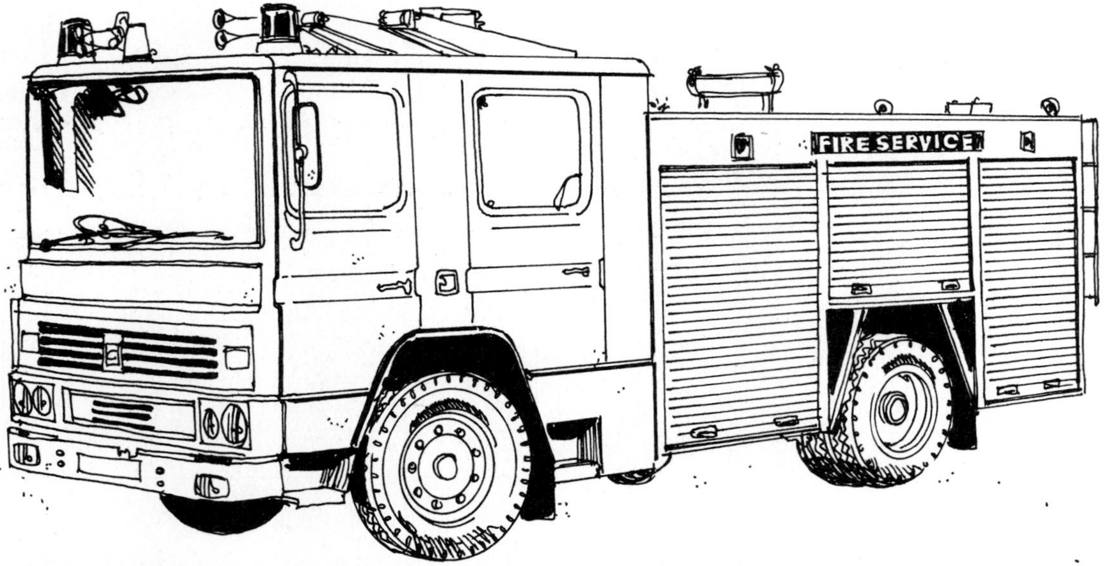

Pull the coaches

The engine shown here is too small to pull the coaches.

✤ Design a bigger engine to pull them.

✤ Draw a sketch of your engine below to give you an idea of the size it should be.

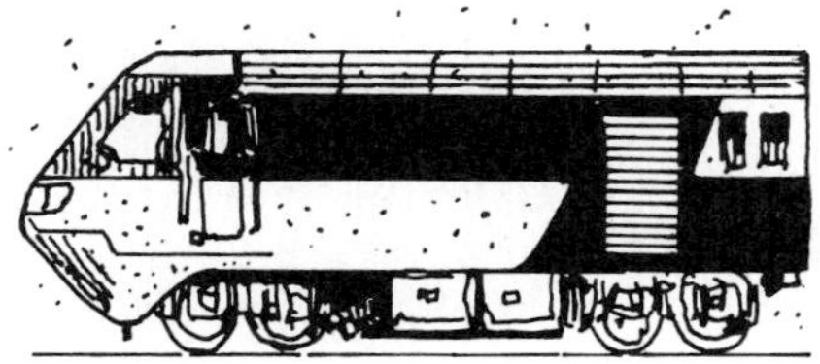

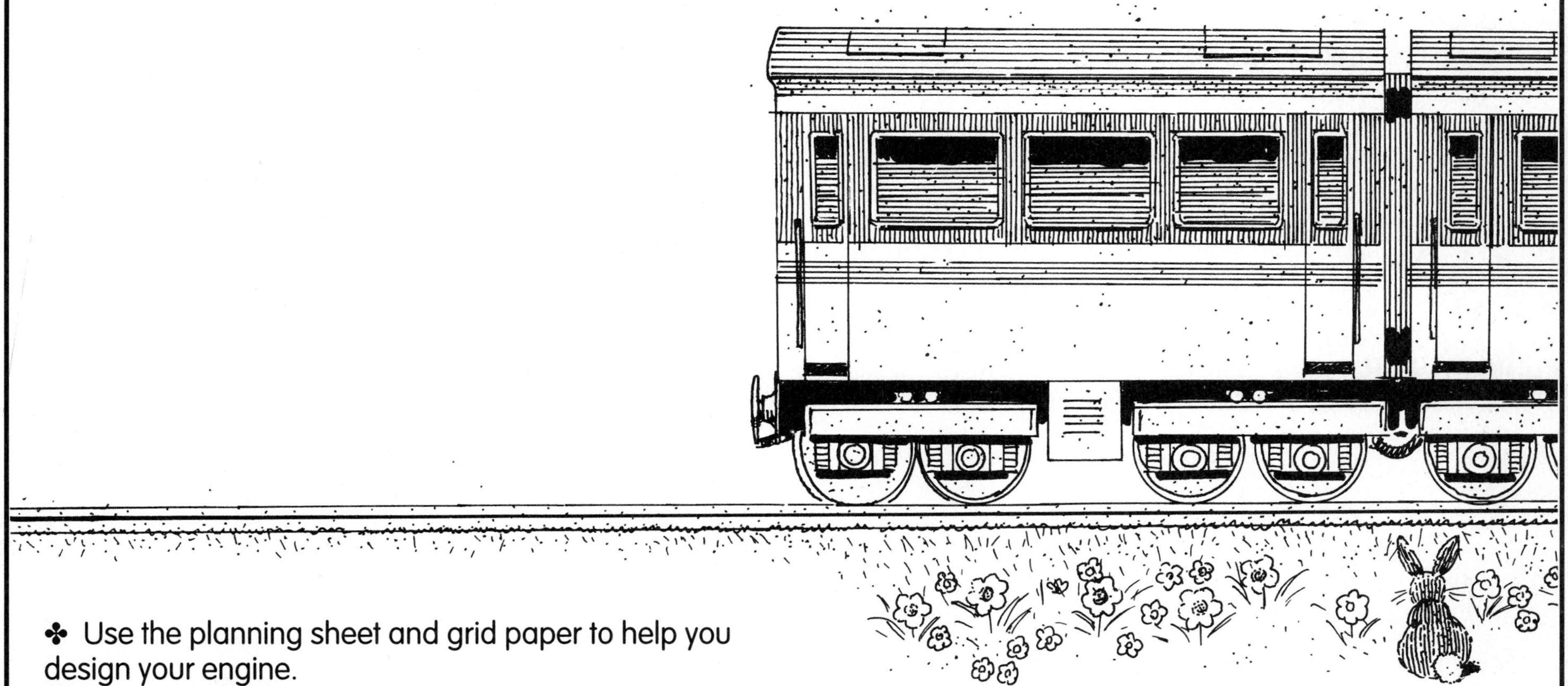

✤ Use the planning sheet and grid paper to help you design your engine.

✤ Make a model of your engine and test it.

Name ____________________

A flat tyre

A flat tyre

✤ Cut out the eight pictures opposite and put them in order.

✤ Stick them on to a separate sheet of paper.

✤ Now write a set of instructions for changing a wheel on a car.
The pictures below may help explain some of the tools.

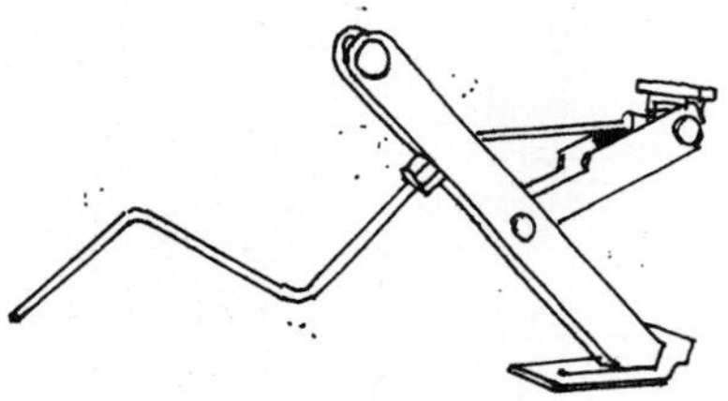

This is called a jack.
It is used to lift up the car.

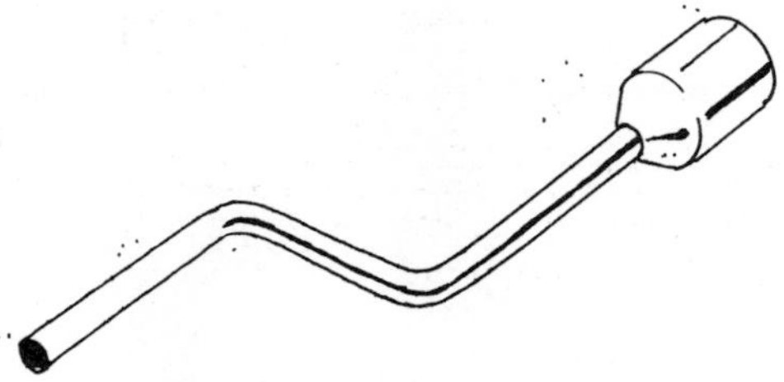

This is a wheel brace.
It is used to undo the wheel nuts.

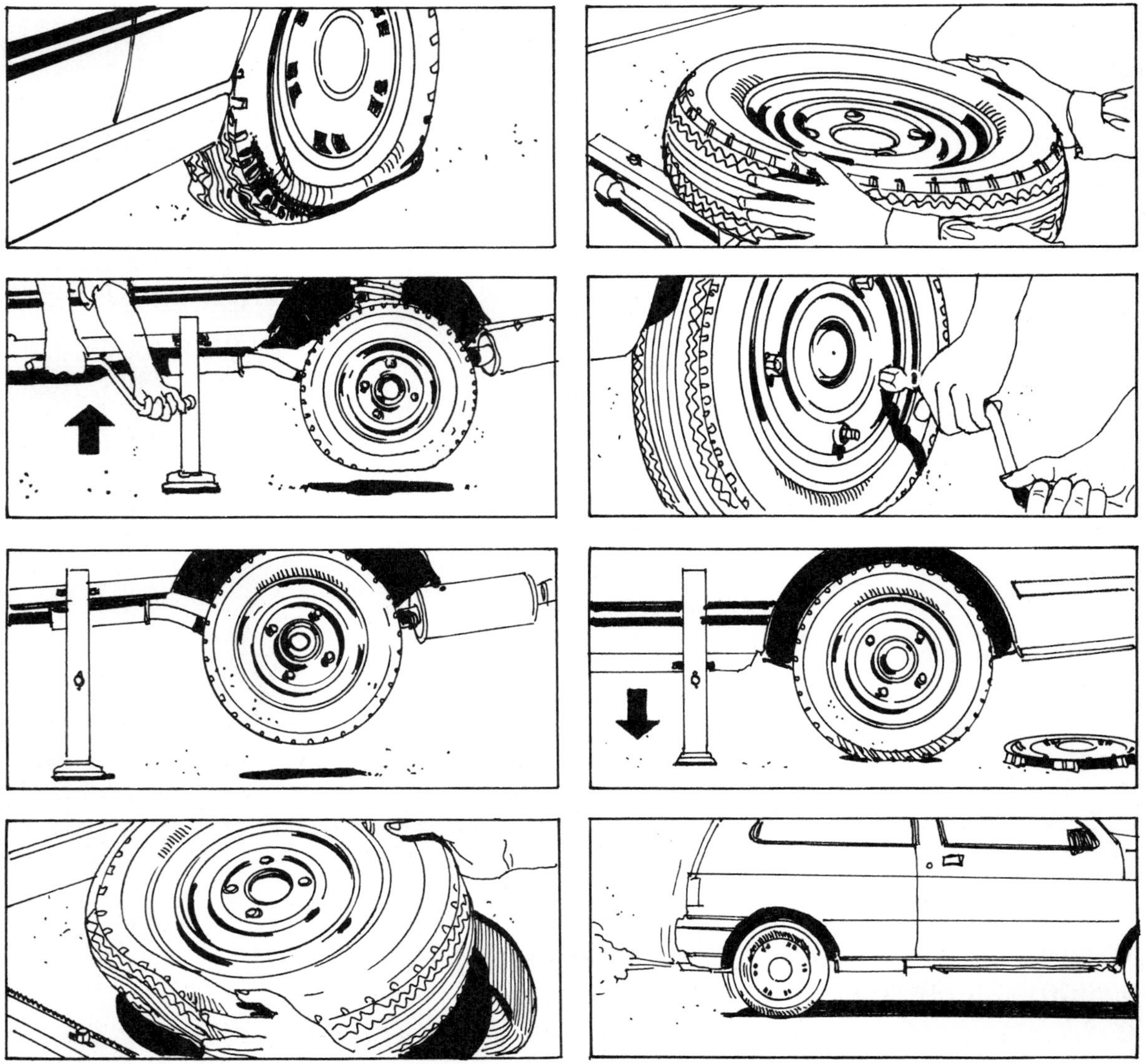

Name ____________________

Design a sail pattern

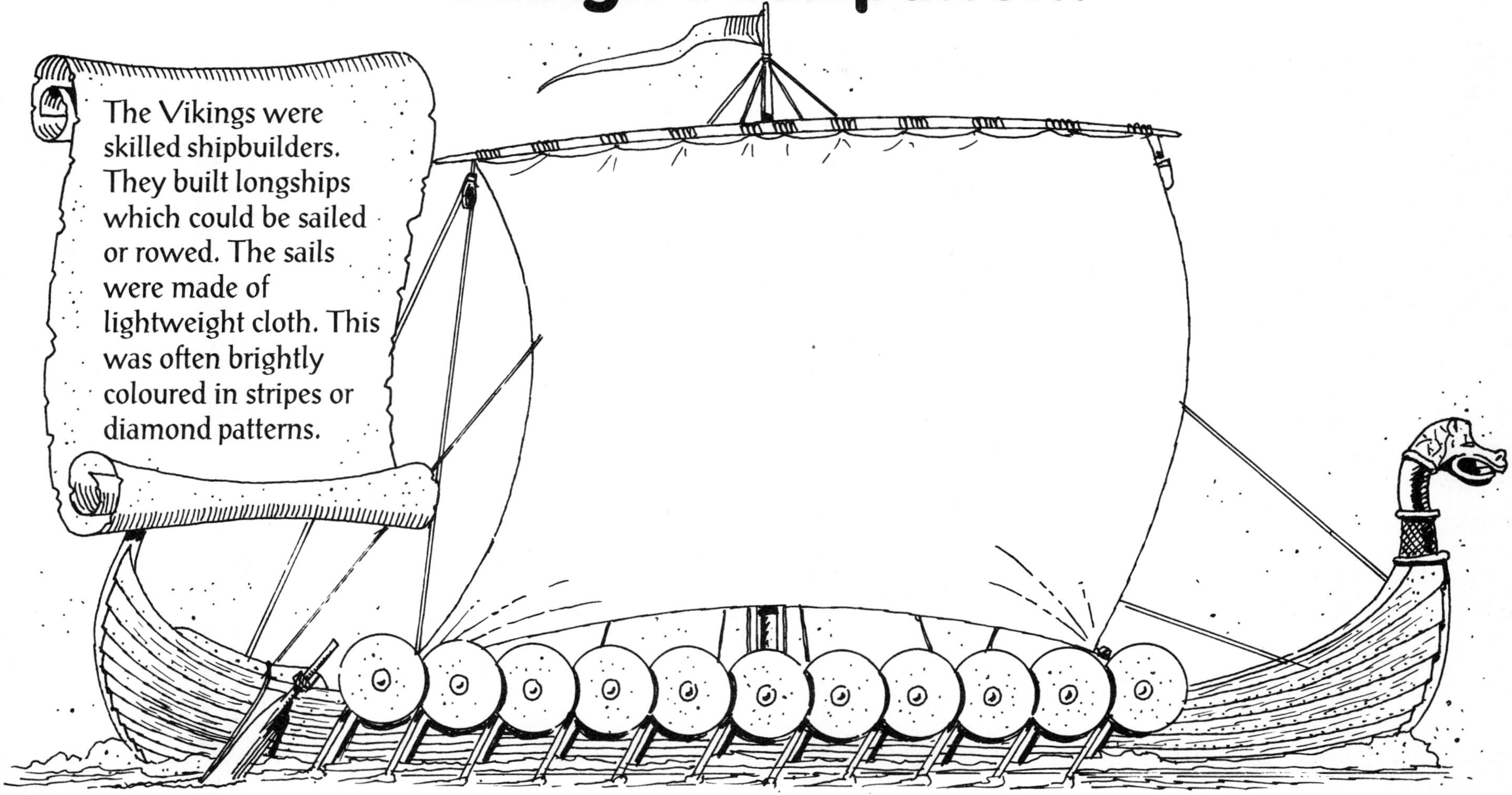
The Vikings were skilled shipbuilders. They built longships which could be sailed or rowed. The sails were made of lightweight cloth. This was often brightly coloured in stripes or diamond patterns.

- ✤ Design a sail for this Viking longship.
- ✤ Use the planning sheet for your rough designs.
- ✤ Draw your final version on this sheet.
- ✤ Find out about the figurehead of a ship. Design one for this Viking ship.

Name ____________________

Journey into space

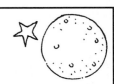

You are a space traveller who has landed on an unknown planet.

✤ In the space provided draw a map of how the planet looked as you approached it from space.

- What shape is the planet?
- Is there any water on it?
- Can you see any vegetation? Where is it?
- Are there any dwellings on it?

✤ Now make a model of the surface of the planet. You could use a strong sheet of card as the base. You could make the hills from screwed up pieces of newspaper and cover the whole surface with strips of papier mâché. What other materials will you use?

Name ____________________

Seafarer's alphabet

Here are some words connected with ships and sea travel.

aft	hammock	yard	figurehead	deck	sextant	log	jib
rudder	port	bow	grog	freeboard	keel	mast	
timbers	quay	navigate	caulking	bulwark	oar	voyage	

✤ Find out what each one means and make a seafarer's dictionary. Remember to put the words with their definitions in alphabetical order. Can you add any of your own seafaring words?

Word	Definitions

Name ______________________

Meshing cogs

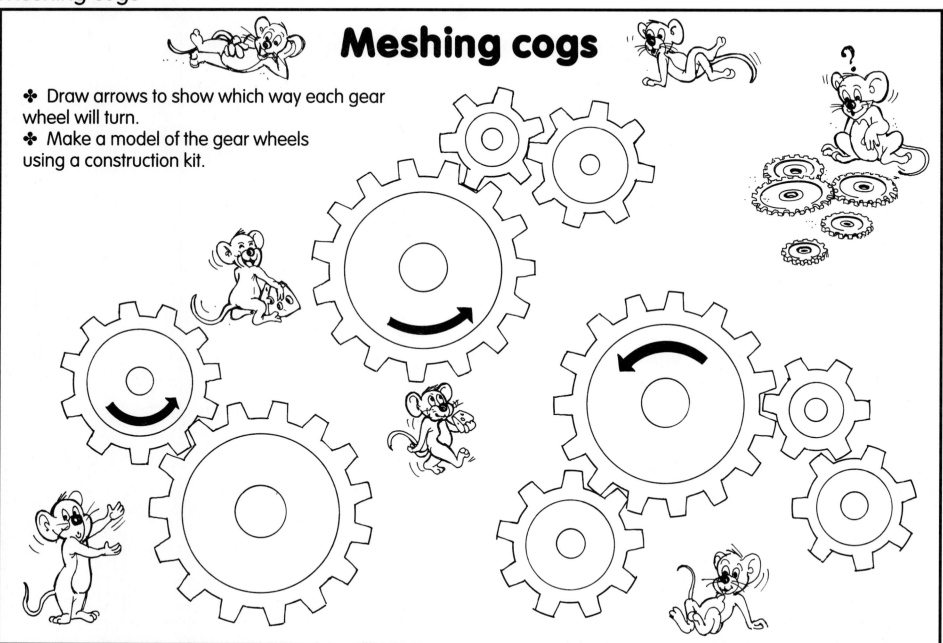

✤ Draw arrows to show which way each gear wheel will turn.
✤ Make a model of the gear wheels using a construction kit.

Name ____________________

Ice-cream island

You are a travel agent specialising in unusual locations. You want to encourage holiday makers to visit Ice-cream Island.

✤ Design and make a travel brochure advertising holidays to the island.

✤ Use this page to list the aspects you want to include.

- Are there any places of special interest?
- What is the weather like?
- Where will visitors stay?
- What is the currency?

✤ Use the flat plan sheet to help with your organisation.

Name ____________

Going by train

Going by train

What would be the best route and changes for a train between:

- ✤ London to Liverpool before 14.00 hrs
- ✤ Liverpool to Great Yarmouth before 17.00 hrs
- ✤ Newcastle to Exeter before 16.00 hrs

Use the train time tables to help you.

- ✤ How long will each journey take? Work out the cost of each journey using the information given.

North Western Line			
London	06.00	09.00	10.00
Oxford	X	10.00	11.00
Birmingham	07.25	X	12.00
Manchester	08.15	X	13.00
Liverpool	09.00	11.15	13.30
Liverpool	09.30	11.30	14.00
Manchester	10.15	X	14.30
Birmingham	11.05	X	15.30
Oxford	X	12.45	16.30
London	12.40	13.45	17.30

North Eastern Line			
London	04.00	06.00	08.00
Birmingham	05.00	07.00	09.00
Leicester	05.20	07.20	09.20
York	06.00	08.00	13.30
Newcastle	08.00	10.00	14.00
Newcastle	08.30	10.20	14.30
York	10.30	12.30	15.30
Leicester	11.10	13.10	16.30
Birmingham	11.30	13.30	15.30
London	12.20	14.20	16.20

South Western Line			
London	06.00	09.00	14.00 *
Oxford	06.30	09.30	X
Weymouth	07.30	10.30	X
Exeter	09.00	12.00	15.30
Exeter	09.05	13.00	17.00
Weymouth	10.35	14.30	X
Oxford	11.35	15.30	X
London	12.05	16.00	18.30

South Eastern Line				
London	06.00	12.00	13.30	14.00
Harlow	06.45	12.40	14.10	14.30
Norwich	X	13.20	X	15.15
Gt Yarmouth	X	14.00	13.00	16.00
Dover	07.55	X	15.30	X
Dover	08.15	X	16.30	X
Gt Yarmouth	X	14.30	X	17.00
Norwich	X	15.00	X	17.45
Harlow	09.05	16.00	16.50	18.30
London	09.50	16.30	17.30	19.00

X = train doesn't visit this station

All trains travel on all days

* = Express

Name ____________________

Planning a Roman road

You are a Roman surveyor who has been given a copy of this map of an area newly conquered by the army. Your task is to plan a road route from X to Y.

✤ Show on the map the route your road would take.

✤ Write instructions for the engineers on a separate sheet, using grid references.

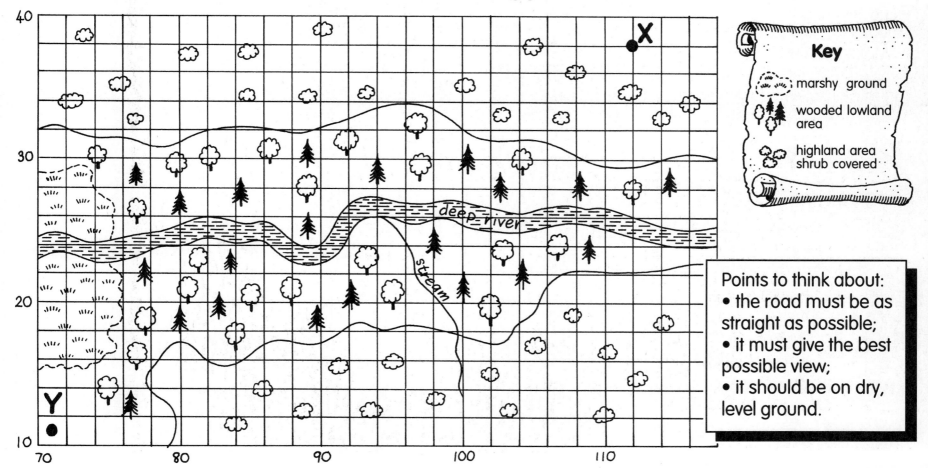

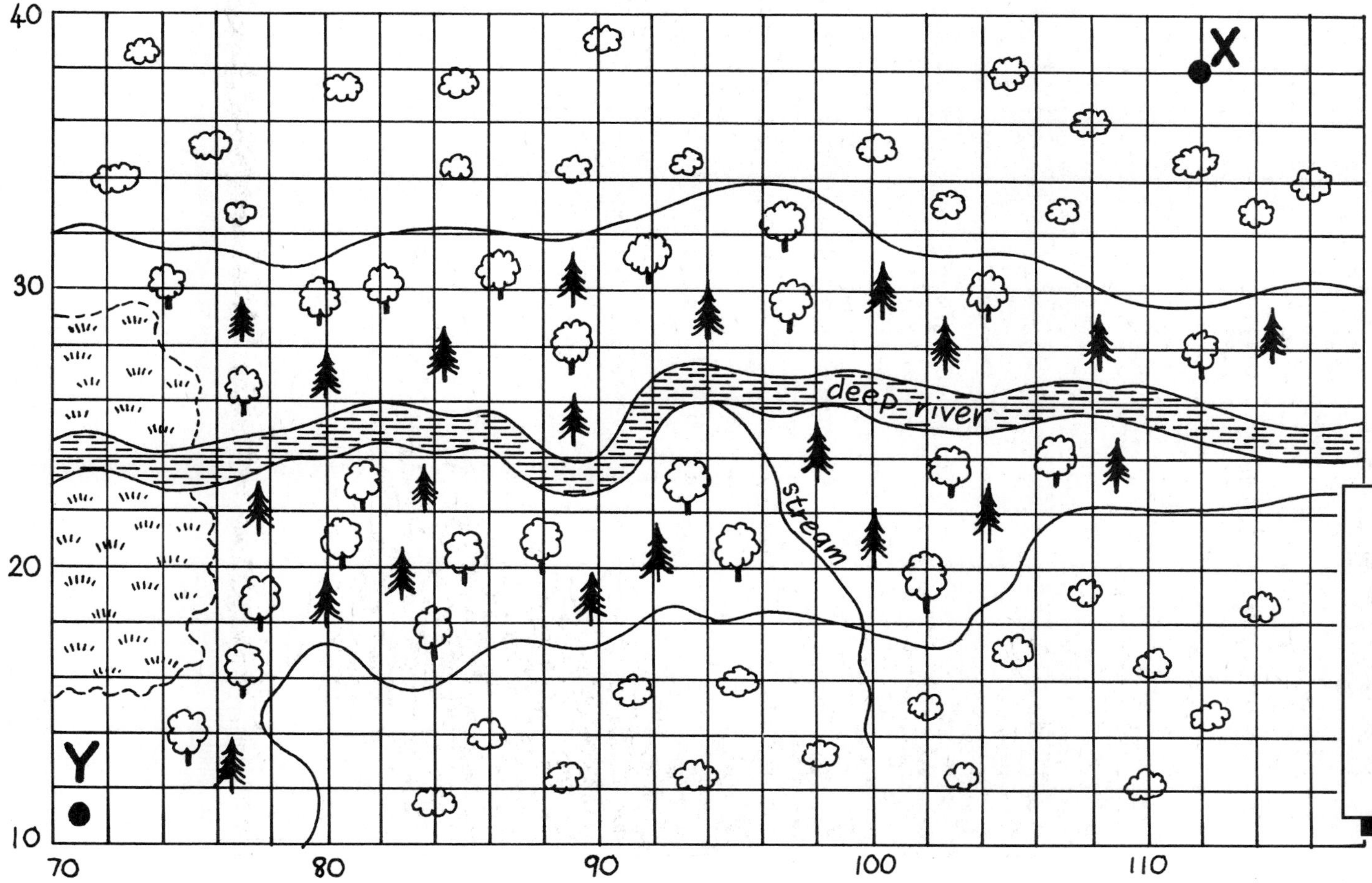

Points to think about:

- the road must be as straight as possible;
- it must give the best possible view;
- it should be on dry, level ground.

Name ____________________

Safety first

✤ Make a booklet for young children about keeping safe on the roads.

• Is your booklet going to be for children as pedestrians? Or cyclists? Or car passengers?

• What aspects of road safety will you need to include?

✤ Make a list of topics on this sheet.

✤ Use the flat plan sheet to help you plan your booklet. You might like to include some of the signs below.

My list

A milestone

There are many different types of road signs. In Roman times milestones were placed along roads at distances of 1,000 paces (a Roman mile is about 1,480 metres). The milestones showed the distance to the nearest town and the name of the emperor ruling at the time. The distances are written in Roman numerals.

✤ Design your own milestone below. Include useful facts travellers to your area might need. For example:

- How far to your nearest chemist or newsagent?
- When was the road built?
- What is the road called?
- Who was king or queen when the road was built?

✤ Are there any other useful details that you could add? You will need to research the facts.

✤ Use the planning sheet to plan how you would make your milestone. Make it if you can.

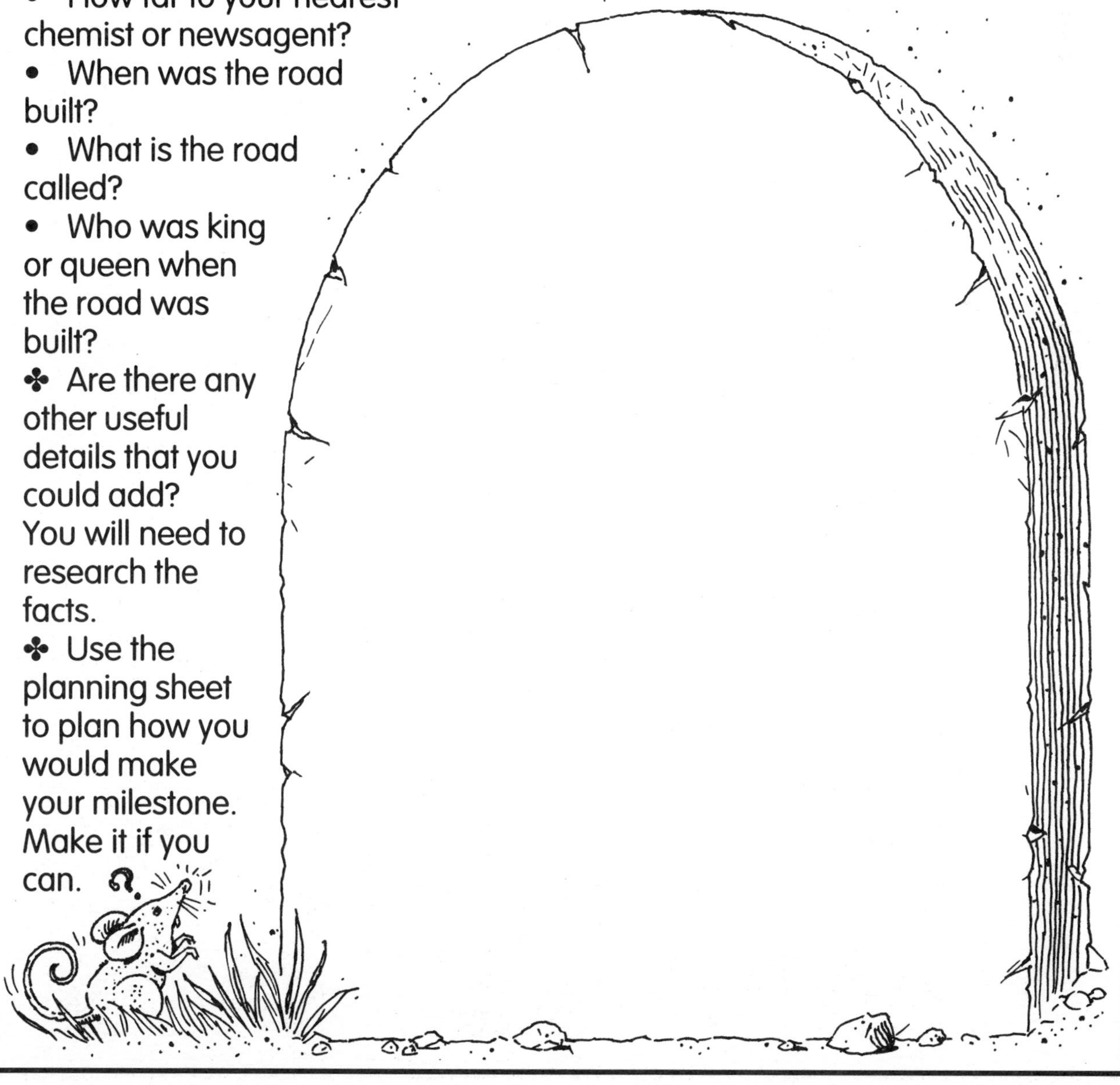

Name ____________

Voyage of exploration

You are a sea captain on a voyage of exploration. You have discovered a new country and are going to draw a map of it.

✤ List all the things that you want to put on the map.

My list

✤ Now draw your map of this new place.

✤ What will you name this place you have discovered and why?

✤ On the back of this sheet write some instructions to show other people how to find the country. Use the planning sheet to help you.

✤ Design and make a waterproof case that will store your map safely on the journey home.

Name ____________________

Finding the way

✤ Plan a system of signs to direct visitors around your school, starting from the main entrance.
✤ First, list the places they will need to know about.
✤ Now use the grid paper to draw a plan of the general layout of the school and put these places on it. Indicate where you think signs are needed.
✤ On the planning sheet, design your system of signs. Decide what labels will be required, what should go at the entrance and how you will indicate directions.
✤ Now make your system.

My list

Name ____________________

Garage forecourt

Here are plan views of items found on a petrol filling station forecourt.

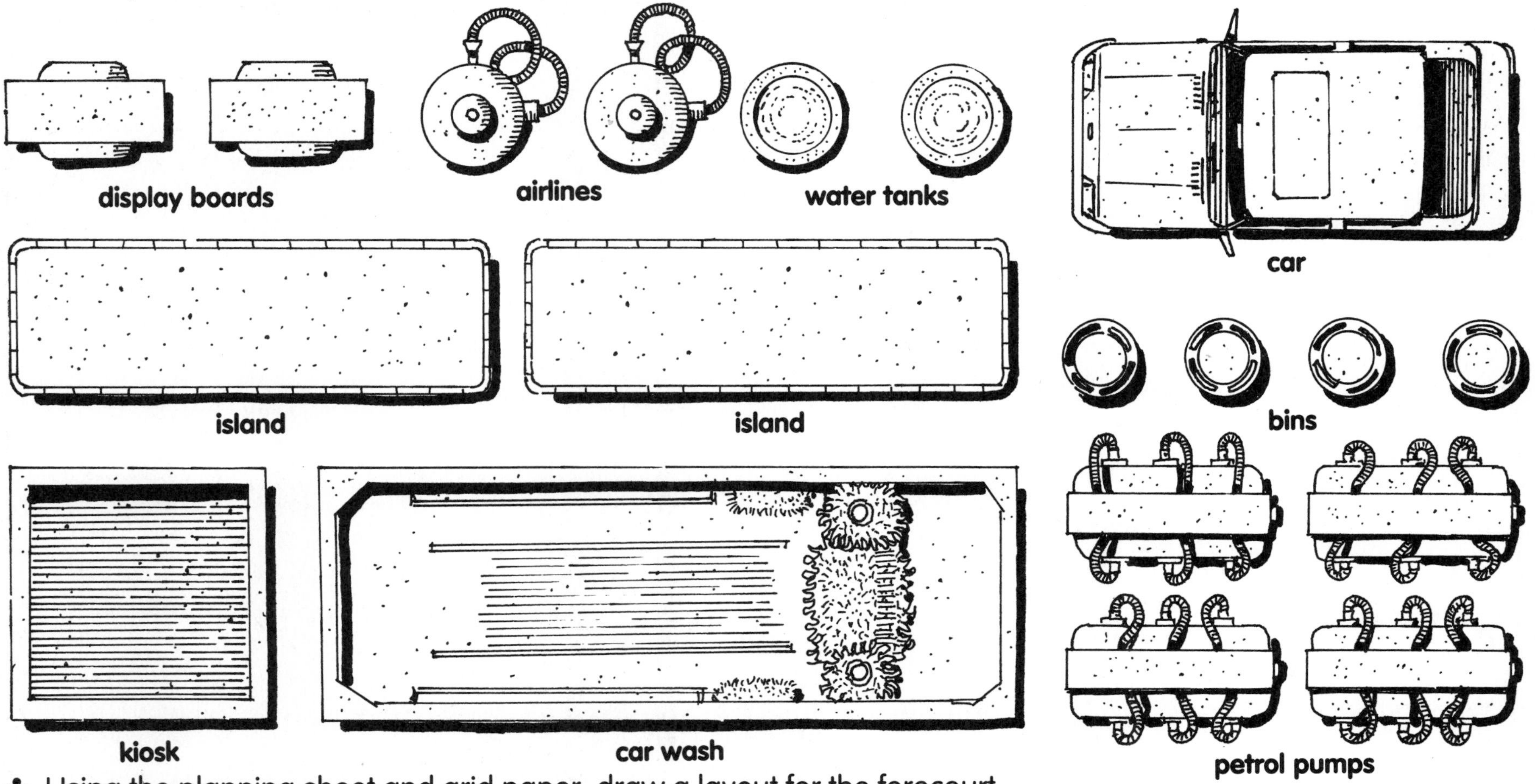

✤ Using the planning sheet and grid paper, draw a layout for the forecourt.
Make sure that drivers can access all the facilities safely.
Remember not to block access to the other petrol pumps when one of them is being used.

Cut down on cars

Roads in big towns and cities are becoming more and more congested with cars.

✤ Produce a 90-second tape for a local radio campaign to encourage people not to use their cars for travelling to work.

✤ Write below the points you want to include. Then use your notes to write out the script on another sheet.

Reasons for not using cars

Alternative forms of transport

Narrow-boat living space

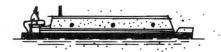

Until the 1950s, many families lived and worked on narrow boats. These were boats designed to carry goods such as coal, stone, food or paper, along the canals. The living quarters were small.

- Design a space-saving layout for a narrow-boat family. The space you have is 2m wide x 3m long x 2m high. You will need to include space for sleeping, cooking, washing and storage.
- Cut out the shapes below to make your planning easier.
- Draw your design to scale on the grid paper.

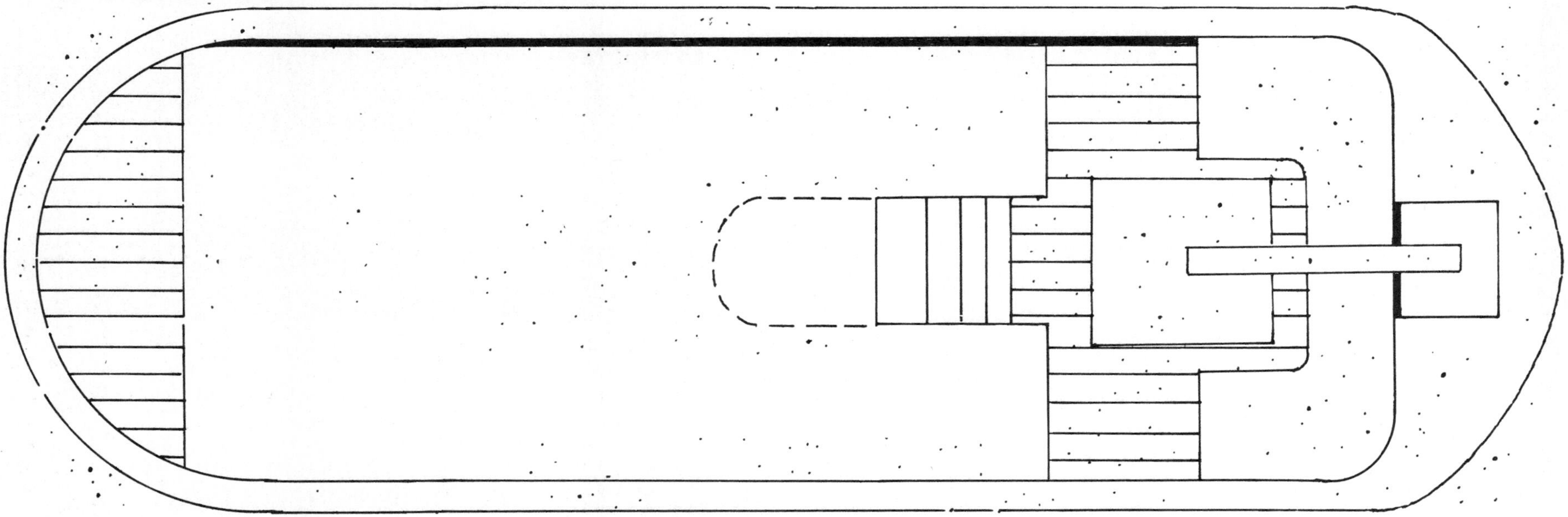

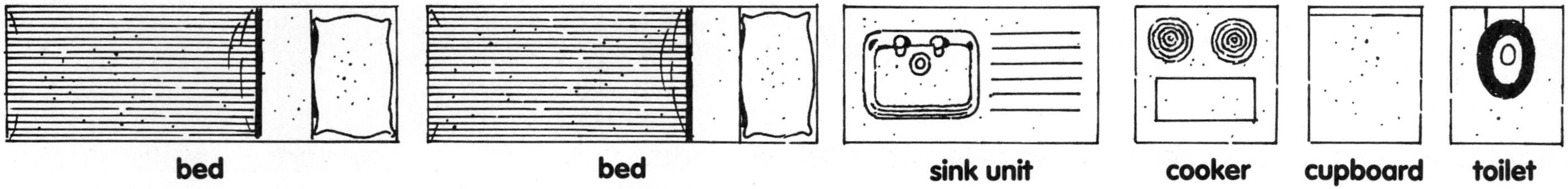

Evacuation

During the first week of September 1939, 100,000 children were sent from the cities in Britain to live in the countryside. World War II had begun. Why do you think these children had to be evacuated?

✤ List some reasons below.

My list

What information would need to be given to each family that was going to look after a child?

✤ Design a label in the space below that would supply this information. What headings will you use for the details?

The children were limited to what they could take. It must all fit in one small case and had to include clothes, a packed lunch and a gas mask.

✤ List what you would have taken with you.

Name ______________________

Move it!

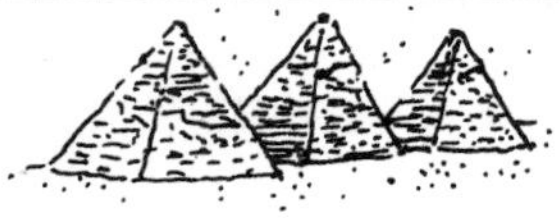

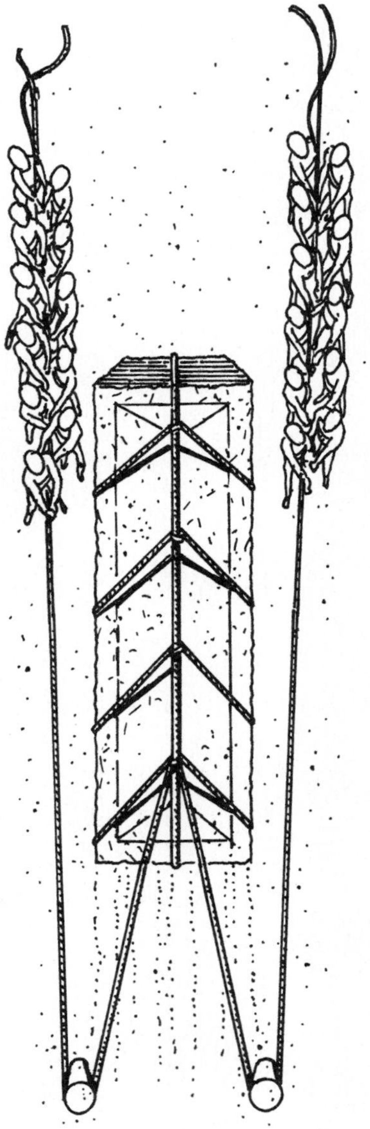

When the Ancient Egyptians were building the pyramids, they had to transport huge blocks of stone across the land to the building sites.

✤ Using a house brick to represent a block of stone, investigate ways of moving it along without touching it. The pictures here will give you some ideas. Could you use pencils to help you?

✤ List some methods that might be used and the materials you will need.

Other methods	Materials

✤ Choose your best method. Give instructions in pictures to show an Ancient Egyptian builder how best to move the heavy stone blocks. Do this on the flat plan sheet.

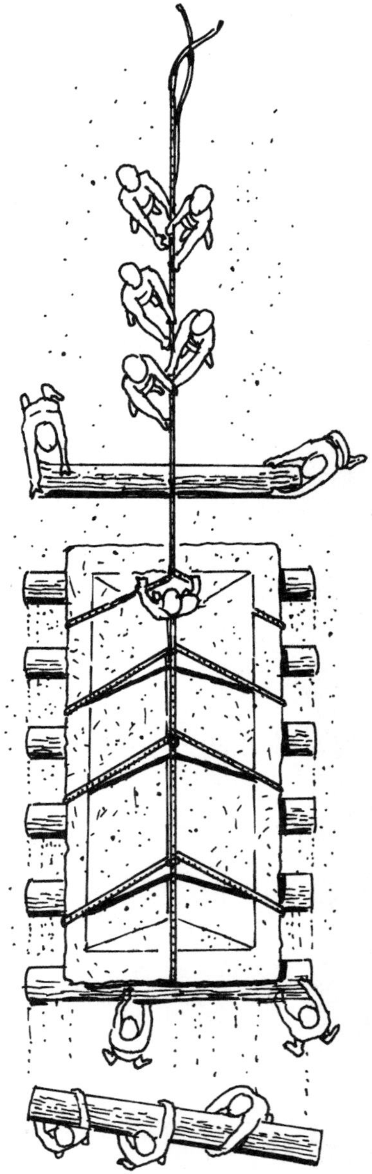

Name ______________________

Planning sheet for ______________________

team	materials	objective

things to include:

design

Name ____________________

Testing sheet

Testing sheet for ____________________

Questions to be asking/things to be testing

Test	**Results/findings**

Evaluation/decision

Name ____________________

Self evaluation sheet

Group members ____

Problem ____

____

How did you work?	well	quite well	not so well
Did you help the group?	yes	a little	not really
How well did you plan before starting your work?	well	a little	not enough
Did you choose suitable materials?	yes	no	
Did you have enough time?	yes	no	
Did you enjoy the activity?	yes	OK	no

Any other comments: ____

Name ____________________

Model figure template

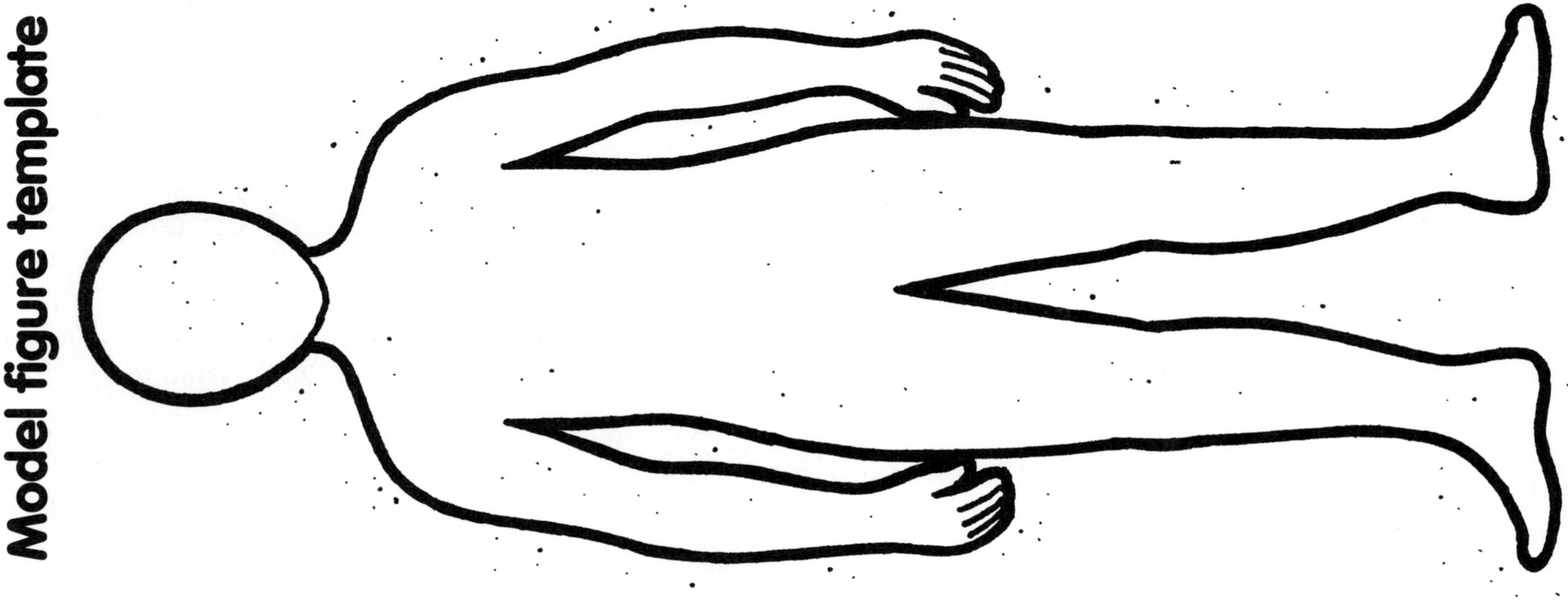

Name ____________________

Flat plan

Title____________________________

Name ____________________

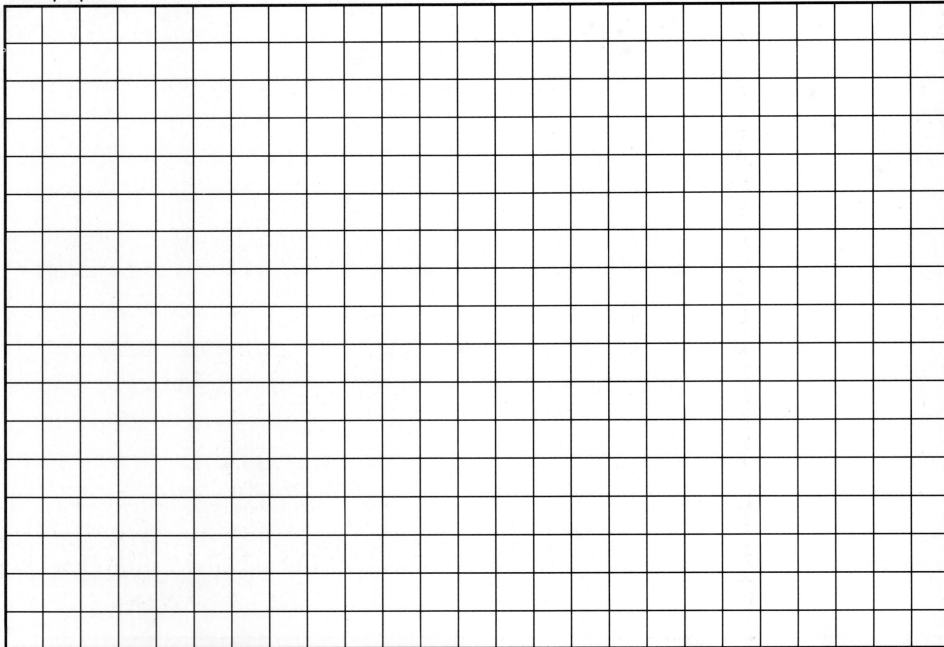

Grid paper